SCOURING OF THE WHITE HORSE

THE
SCOURING OF THE WHITE HORSE;

OR, THE

Long Vacation Ramble of a London Clerk.

BY

THOMAS HUGHES

OLD AND NEW.

See how the Autumn leaves float by, decaying,
  Down the red whirls of yon rain-swollen stream ;
So fleet the works of men, back to their earth again ;
  Ancient and holy things fade like a dream.

Nay! see the Spring blossoms steal forth a-maying,
  Clothing with tender buds orchard and glen ;
So, though old forms go by, ne'er can their spirit die,
  Look! England's bare boughs show green leaf again.—KINGSLEY.

ILLUSTRATED BY RICHARD DOYLE.

ALAN SUTTON
1989

ALAN SUTTON PUBLISHING
BRUNSWICK ROAD · GLOUCESTER

First Published 1859 by Macmillan and Co.

First published in this edition 1989.

British Library Cataloguing in Publication Data

Hughes, Thomas, *1822–1896*
    The scouring of the white horse.
    1. Oxfordshire. Uffington. Hiss figures.
    Uffington White Horse
    I. Title
    942.5'76

ISBN 0 86299 563 9

Typesetting and origination by
Alan Sutton Publishing Limited
Printed in Great Britain by
The Guernsey Press Company Limited,
Guernsey, Channel Islands

PREFACE

HE great success of the festival (or 'pastime', as it is called in the neighbourhood) which was held on White Horse Hill on the 17th and 18th of September, 1857, to celebrate the 'Scouring of the Horse', according to immemorial custom, led the Committee of Management to think that our fellow-county-men at least, if not our countrymen generally, would be glad to have some little printed memorial, which should comprise not only an account of the doings on the Hill on the late occasion, but should also endeavour to gather up the scattered legends and traditions of the country side, and any authentic historical notices relating to the old monument, of which we west-countrymen are all so fond and proud.

I had the good or ill luck (as the case may be) to be the only member of the Committee whose way of life had led him into the perilous paths of literature; so the task of compiling and editing our little book was laid on my shoulders.

Installed as chronicler to the White Horse, I entered with no ill will on my office, having been all my life possessed, as is the case with so many Englishmen, by intense local attachment, love for every stone and turf of the country where I was born and bred. But it is one thing to have zeal, and another to have discretion; and when I came to consider my materials, I found that the latter quality would be greatly needed. For, what were they? One short bright gleam of history from the writings of old monks a thousand years ago; traditions and dim legends, which I and most Berkshire men have always faithfully believed from our youth up, and shall go on believing to our dying day, but which we could hardly put before general readers in serious narrative; a dry notice here and there by some old antiquary of the seventeenth or eighteenth century; stories floating in the memories of old men still living; small broad-sheets from country town presses, with lists of the competitors for prizes at rustic games, newspaper articles, remarks by Committee-men and umpires, scraps of antiquarian lore, abuse of the Great Western Railway for not allowing the trains to stop, bits of vernacular dialogue, and odd rhymes. What could be done with them all? How out of the mass could a shapely book be called out, fit to be laid before a fastidious British public, not born in Berkshire?

Not exactly seeing how this was to be done, the only course which remained, was to follow the example of a good housewife in the composition of that excellent food called 'stir-about' – throw them all together into the pot, stir them round and round with a great spoon, and trust that the look of the few great raisins, and the flavour of the allspice, may leaven the mass, and make it pleasing to the eye and palate; and so, though the stir-about will never stand up in a china dish by itself, it may, we hope, make a savoury and pleasant side dish, in a common soup tureen.

The raisins, and those of the best quality, have been furnished by the great artist who has kindly undertaken to give us pictures; the allspice has been contributed by the Committee and other kind friends, and I have done the milk and meal, and the stirring. The responsibility therefore rests with me, though the credit, whatever it may be, rests with others. But let me insist here, at once, that if there be any failure in the dish, it is the fault of the dresser and not of the subject-matter.

For, suppose an intelligent Englishman to be travelling in France, and to find the whole population in the neighbourhood of Tours turning out in their best clothes for a two days' holiday on a high hill, upon which the rude figure of a huge hammer is roughly sculptured. On inquiry, he finds that the figure has been there long before the memory of the oldest man living, but it has always been carefully preserved and kept fresh; and although there is no printed history of how it came there, yet that all neighbouring men, of whatever degree, associate it with the name of Charles Martel and his great victory over the Saracens, and are ready one and all to rejoice over it, and to work and pray that it may go down to their children looking as it does now. Or, to come to much later times, let our traveller find an eagle cut out on a hill in Hungary, similarly honoured, and associated with the name of Eugene, and the memory of the day

> When, the old black eagle flying,
> All the Paynim powers defying,
> On we marched, and stormed Belgrade.

Should we not thank him for giving us the best account he could of the figure, the festival, and all the traditions connected with them; and think he had fallen on a very note-worthy matter, and well worth the telling when he got back to England?

Well, here we have the same thing at our own doors; a rude colossal figure cut out in the turf, and giving the name to a whole district; legends connecting it with the name of our greatest king, and with his great victory over the Pagans, and a festival which has been held at very short intervals ever since the ninth century. Rich as our land is in historical monuments, there is none more remarkable than the White Horse; and in this belief we put forth this little book in his honour, hoping that it may perhaps fix upon him, and the other antiquities which surround him, the attention of someone who can bring science and knowledge to bear upon the task to which we can only bring good will.

For, alas! let me confess at once, that in these qualities our book is like to be sadly deficient. The compiler has no knowledge whatever of the Anglo-Saxon tongue, or of Saxon or other antiquities. There is indeed of necessity a semblance of learning and research about the chapter which tells the history of the battle of Ashdown, because the materials for it had to be collected from a number of old chroniclers, whose names will be found in the foot-notes. But any fifth-form boy, with industry enough to read about 200 small pages of monkish Latin, may master the whole for himself in the originals in a week; and for those who cannot do this, there is the jubilee edition of the chroniclers, put forth by the Alfred Committee in 1852, where a translation of the old fellows will be found in parallel columns, together with much learning concerning them and their times, in foot-note, preface, and appendix. This translation I have followed in all but a few passages, in which the text used by the translators has probably differed from the one which I have seen. For the Saxon Chronicle, I have used Ingram's translation.

But while we do not pretend to be antiquaries, or historians, or learned men, we do claim to be honest average Englishmen, and will yield to no man in our love for our own quiet corner of the land of our birth. We do think, that whatever deeply interests us cannot fail in a degree to interest our countrymen. We are sure that reverence for all great Englishmen, and a loving remembrance of the great deeds done by them in old times, will help to bring to life in us the feeling that we are a family, bound together to work our God's purposes in this little island, and in the uttermost parts of the earth; to make clear to us the noble inheritance which we have in common; and to sink into their proper place the miserables trifles, and odds and ends, over which we are so apt to wrangle. We do hope that our example will lead Englishmen of other counties to cherish every legend and story which hangs round any nook of the neighbourhood, connecting it with the times and the men who have gone before; to let no old custom, which has a meaning, however rude, die out, if it can be kept alive; and not to keep either legend or custom to themselves, but (like us) to put them in the best shape they can, and publish them for the benefit of their countrymen; we of the White Horse Committee, at any rate, hereby pledging ourselves to read all such publications.

I must here take the opportunity of specially thanking three of my fellow Committee-men, and two other friends, for the trouble they have taken in various ways to lighten my work. If this book at all fulfils the objects for which it has been written, the thanks of my readers, as well as my own, will be due to

E. M. ATKINS, Esq., of Kingstone Lisle
Mr WILLIAM WHITFIELD, of Uffington
Mr HEBER HUMFREY, of Kingstone Farm; and to
JOHN Y. AKERMAN,Esq., Secretary of the Society of Antiquaries; and
Mr LUKE LONSLEY, of Hampsted Norris, Berks.

And now, without further preface, we commend our 'stir-about' to Englishmen in general, and west-countrymen in particular.

CHAPTER I

ICHARD, said our governor, as I entered his room at five o'clock on the afternoon of the 31st of August, 1857, running his pen down the columns of the salary-book, 'your quarter-day today I think? Let me see; you were raised to £ a-year in February last, – so much for quarter's salary, and so much for extra work. I am glad to see that you have been working so steadily; you'll deserve your holiday, and enjoy it all the more. You'll find that all right, I think;' and he pushed a small paper across the table towards me, on which my account was stated in our cashier's hand, and looked at me over his spectacles.

My heart jumped at the mention of my holiday; I just ran my eye down the figures, and was glad to find the total a pound or two higher than I had expected. For I had lately learnt shorthand, and had been taking notes for our firm, for which I found they allowed me extra pay.

'Quite right, Sir,' I said; 'and I'm sure I'm much obliged to you, Sir, for letting me do the extra work, because –'

'Well, never mind that,' said he, with a little laugh; 'I shouldn't give you the extra work, Richard, if it didn't suit me, or if I could get it better done anywhere else; so the account's all square on that point. There's your money.'

And he pushed over to me a very nice sum of money. I dare say you would like to know what it was, reader. Now I'm not going to tell you. Why should you know just what my income is? I don't owe you or any one else five shillings, and have a very tidy account at the savings' bank, besides having paid for all the furniture and books in my room, not very far from Lambsconduit Street, which I reckon to be worth fifty pounds of any man's money; so you see my income is enough to keep me before the world, and I wish more of you could say as much.

'I'm very much obliged, Sir,' said I again, as I wrote a receipt over a stamp which I took out of my pocket-book, and stuck on to the bottom of the account.

'No, you're not,' said our governor, quite short; 'it's your own money, fairly earned. You're not obliged to any man for giving you what's your own.' He is such an odd fellow about these things. But mind you, I think he's quite right too; for after all, no doubt each of us earns a good penny for him over and above what he pays us, else why should he keep us on? but somehow, one can't help thanking anyone who pays one money; at least, I can't.

'Now, as to your holiday,' went on our governor. 'There's Jobson went for his fortnight on the 30th; he'll be back on the 14th of September at latest. You can take any time you like, after that.'

'Then, Sir,' said I directly, 'I should like it as soon as possible.'

'Very well,' said he; 'Tuesday the 15th to Tuesday the 29th of September, both inclusive;' and he made a note in another book which lay on his desk. 'Good evening, Richard.'

'Good evening, Sir,' said I; and away I went down to our room in as good spirits as any young fellow in our quarter of London.

Of course all the clerks began shouting at once to know how much money I'd got, and when I was going to have my holiday. Well, I didn't tell them what money I had, any more than I've told you, because I like to keep my own counsel about such matters. Besides, there are several of our clerks whose ways I don't at all like; so I don't do anything I can help which might look as if I liked them. No! hands off, is my motto with these sort of chaps.

I'm sure there's no pride about me, though. My name's Easy, and always was; and I like every fellow, whatever his coat is, who isn't always thinking about the cut of it, or what he has in the pocket of it. But, goodness knows, I can't stand a fellow who gives himself airs, and thinks himself a chalk above everybody who can't dress and do just as he can. Those chaps, I always see, are just the ones to do lickspittle to those that they think have more in their pockets than themselves.

But I must get on with my story, for you don't all want to know my opinions about the clerks in our office, I dare say.

Well, when I got down, as I said before, we were all just on the move (business hours being from nine till six in our office), taking down coats and hats, and clearing desks for the night, so I just sidled up to Jem Fisher, and little Neddy Baily, who are the two I like best, and told them to come up to my room to supper at eight o'clock, which they of course were very glad to promise to do, and then I went off to get ready for them.

Jem Fisher and I are both very fond of a dish which I believe very few of you ever heard of. One Sunday in May, a year or two back, he and I had been down beyond Notting Hill, listening to the nightingales; and coming back we walked through Kensington Gardens, and came out at the gate into the Notting Hill Road close to Hyde Park. We were late, for us, so we hailed a 'bus, and got on the box. The driver was full of talk about all the fine people he had been seeing walking in the gardens that afternoon, and seemed to think it hard he couldn't enjoy himself just as they did. 'However, gentlemen,' said he at last, 'there's some things as the haristocracy ain't alive to. Did you ever eat cow-heel?' Perhaps Jem, who had all his best clothes on, didn't mind being taken for one of the aristocracy; at least just for a minute, for he's too good a fellow to like being taken for anybody but himself when he comes to think of it; at any rate, he and I took to eating cow-heel from that time. So the first thing I did, after going home and locking up most of my money, and speaking to my landlady, who is the best old soul alive if you take her in her own way, was, to set off to Clare Market, and buy some cow-heel and sausages; and on my way back through the Turnstile, I thought, as it was so hot, I would have some fruit too; so I bought a pottle of plums and a piece of a pineapple, and got home.

They came in sharp to time, and I and my landlady had everything ready, and two foaming pewter pots full of bitter beer and porter. So we had a capital supper, and then cleared it all away, and sat down to eat the fruit and have a quiet pipe by the time it began to get dark.

'And so,' said little Neddy (he is only just eighteen, and hasn't been in our office a year yet; but he's such a clever, industrious little chap, that he has gone over the heads of half a dozen of our youngsters, and hasn't stopped yet by a long way), 'you're off on the 15th! wish I was. Well, here's luck anyhow,' said he, nodding to me, and taking a bite out of a slice of pineapple.

'Gentle Shepherd, tell me where?' said Jem Fisher (Jem is very fond of quoting poetry; not that I think half that he quotes is real poetry, only how is one to find him out? Jem is a tall, good-looking fellow, as old as I am, and that's twenty-one last birthday; we came into the office together years ago, and have been very thick ever since, which I sometimes wonder at, for Jem is a bit of a swell – Gentleman Jem they call him in the office). 'Now, Dick, where are you bound for?'

'Well, that's more than I know myself,' said I.

'Then,' said he, taking his pipe out of his pocket and filling it, 'I vote we settle for him, eh, Neddy?'

'Aye, aye, Sir,' said Neddy, stretching over for the pottle; 'but, I say, Jem, you haven't finished all those plums?' and he poked about in the leaves with his fingers.

'Every mother's son of them,' said Jem, lighting a lucifer; 'if you come to that, Master Ned, hand me over some of that pineapple. But now, about the tour; how much money are you going to spend on it, Dick?'

'Well, I haven't quite settled,' said I; 'but I shouldn't mind, now, going as high as four or five pounds, if I can suit myself.'

'You may go pretty near to Jericho for that now-a-days,' said Neddy. 'As I came along Holborn tonight, I saw a great placard outside the George and Blue Boar, with "to Llangollen and back 15s." on it. What do you think of that? You'll be turned out at the station there with £4. 5s. in your pocket.'

'Where's Llangollen?' said I.

'Not half-way to Jericho,' shouted Jem, with a laugh. 'Where's Llangollen? Why didn't you ever hear the song of Kitty Morgan, the maid of Llangollen? You're a pretty fellow to go touring.'

'Yes, fifty times,' said I; 'only the song don't tell you where the place is – where is it now?'

'In Wales, of course,' said he, thinking he had me.

'Yes, I know that; but whereabouts in Wales,' said I, 'for Wales is a biggish place. Is it near anything one reads about in books, and ought to go and see?'

'Hanged if I know exactly,' said Jem, puffing away; 'only of course Wales is worth seeing.'

'So is France,' struck in Neddy; 'why, you may go to Paris and stay a fortnight for I don't know how little.'

'Aye, or to Edinburgh or the Lakes,' said Jem.

'I want to have the particulars though,' said I; 'I'm not going to start off to some foreign place, and find myself with no money to spend and enjoy myself with, when I get there.'

'I'll tell you what,' said Neddy, jumping up, 'I'll just run round to the Working Men's College, and borrow a Bradshaw from the secretary. We shall find all the cheap excursions there;' and away he went before we could say a word.

'I say,' said Jem to me, 'how fond he is of bringing up that place; he's always at me to go and enter there.'

'So he is at me,' said I, 'and I think I shall, for he seems to pick up a lot of things there. How sharp he is at figures! and he knows more history and geography ten to one than I do. I'll bet he knew what county Llangollen is in, and something about it too. Let's ask him when he comes back.'

'Catch me!' said Jem; 'he'll look it out on the map on his way back, or ask one of the lecturers.'

'Here you are! look here!' said Neddy, tumbling in with two Bradshaws and a great atlas under his arm; '"unprecedented attraction, pleasure excursions," let me see – Return tickets for Ireland, available for a fortnight. Waterford, 1*l*.16*s*.; Cork, 2*l*.'

'Nonsense!' cried Jem, who had got the other Bradshaw; 'listen here: "Channel Islands (remarkable as being the only remaining Norman possessions of the British crown), second class and fore cabin, 21*s*".'

'"London to Dieppe, return tickets available for fourteen days, second class, 21*s*.",' sung out Ned, from the other Bradshaw.

And away they went, with Brussels, and Bangor, and the Manchester Exhibition, and Plymouth and Glasgow, and the Isle of Man, and Margate and Ramsgate, and the Isle of Wight; and then to Gibraltar and Malta and New York, and all over the world. I sat and smoked my pipe, for 'twas no use trying to settle anything; but presently, when they got tired, we set to work and began to put down the figures. However, that wasn't much better, for there were such a lot of tours to go; and one was a bit too short, and the other too long, and this cost too much, and that too little; so all the beer was gone, and we were no nearer settling anything when eleven o'clock struck.

'Well,' said Jem, getting up and knocking the ashes out of his third pipe, 'I declare it's almost as good as going on a tour oneself, settling it for Dick here.'

'I wish you had settled it,' said I; 'I'm more puzzled than when we began.'

'Heigh-ho, fellows never know when they're well off,' said Neddy; 'now I never get a chance. In my holiday I just go down to the old folk at Romford, and there I stick.'

'They don't indeed,' said I; 'I wonder to hear you talk like that, Ned. Some folks would give all they're worth to have old folk to go to.'

'Well, I didn't mean it,' said he, looking hurt. And I don't believe he did, for a kinder hearted fellow don't live; and I was half sorry I had said what I did say.

'Further deliberation will be necessary,' said Jem, lighting his fourth pipe; 'we'll come again tomorrow night: your bacchy's nearly out, Dick; lay in some bird's eye for tomorrow; real Bristol, do you hear?'

'Time to go, I suppose,' said Ned, getting up and gathering the Bradshaws and atlas together; 'are we to come again tomorrow, Dick?'

'Tomorrow, didst thou say? methought I heard Horatio say tomorrow. Go to; it is a thing of nought,' and Jem clapped on his hat and began ranting in his way; so I broke in –

'I wish you'd hold that noise, and talk sense,' said I.

'Shakespere!' said Jem, stopping short, and pulling up his collar.

'Gammon!' said Neddy, bursting out laughing.

'That's right, Neddy,' said I, 'he's always going off with some of his nonsense, and calling it poetry.'

'I didn't say it was poetry, did I?' said Jem.

'What is it, then?' said I.

'Blank verse,' said he.

'What's the difference?,' said I.

'Go up the mill-dam, fall down slam, dat poetry; go up the mill-dam, fall down whoppo', dat plank verse,' said he. 'Go along nigger – had him dere, nigger,' and he turned in his knees and grinned, like one of those poor beggars who black their faces and go about the street with red striped trowsers, white ties, and banjos.

'You ought to be a nigger yourself, Jem,' said I, 'and I should just like to have the driving of you. There, tumble out with you; it's time for steady folks to turn in.'

So I turned them out and held the candle, while they floundered downstairs, that wretch, Jem, singing. 'There's some 'un in de house wid Dinah,' loud enough to be heard at the Foundling. I was glad to hear my landlady catch him at the bottom of the stairs, and give it him well about 'a respectable house' and 'what she was used to with her gents,' while she opened the door; only I don't see what right she had to give it me all over again next morning at breakfast, and call Jem Fisher a wild young man, and bad company, because that's just what he isn't, only a little noisy sometimes. And as if I'm not to have who I please up to my room without her interfering! I pay my rent regular every month, I know. However, I didn't mind what she said at breakfast time, because I had got a letter from the country. I don't get a letter once a month, and it's very odd this one should have come on this very morning, when I was puzzling where to go for my holiday; and I dare say you'll think so too, when I tell you what it was about. Let's see – here it is in my pocket, so you shall have it whole :–

Elm Close Farm, Berks, August 31, 1857.

Dear Dick, – You know you owe me a visit, for you've never been down here, often as I've asked you, since we was at school together – and I have been up to you for or five times. Now, why I particularly want you to come this month is, because we've got some sport to show you down in these quiet parts, which don't happen every day. You see there's an old White Horse cut out in the side of the highest hill hereabouts (a regular break-neck place it is, and there aint three men in the country as 'll ride along the hill side under the Horse), and many folk sets a good deal of store by it, and seems to think the world 'd come to an end if the horse wasn't kept all straight. May be I'm a bit of that mind myself – anyhow you'll see by the paper inside what's going on; and being a scholar, may be you'll know about the White Horse, and like to come down to a scouring. And I can tell you it will be good fun: for I remember the last, when I was quite a little chap, before I went to school, and I've never seen such games since. You've only got to write and say what train you'll come by, and I'll meet you at the Farringdon-road station in my trap. So, as I aint much of a penman, excuse mistakes, and remember me to Fisher and the others I met at your place; and no more at present from yours truly.

JOSEPH HURST.

P.S. – You must stay as long as you can, and I'll mount you on my young bay colt to see a cub killed.

I shouldn't print Joe's letter whole (and as it is I've put a good deal of the spelling right), only I'm quite sure he'll never read this book, and I hope it may serve as a warning to young fellows to keep up their learning when they go and settle down in the country. For when Joe left the Commercial Academy at Brentford, he could write just as good English as I, and if he had put 'many folks seems to think,' or 'you've only got to write,' in a theme, old Hopkins would have given him a good caning. But nothing wears out learning so quick as living in the country and farming, and Joe came into his farm when he was nineteen, and has been at it ever since. And after all, perhaps, it doesn't much signify, because nobody makes himself better understood than Joe, in one way or another; and if he wasn't a little behindhand in his grammar he wouldn't think much of me perhaps – and one don't mind being taken for a scholar even by those who are not the best judges in the world.

Well, thinks I to myself, as I finished my breakfast, this seems like business. If I go down to Joe's, and stay there all my holiday, the fares will be only seventeen shillings; and, say, a pound for expenses down there; one pound seventeen shillings, say two pounds in all. I shall put three pounds into my pocket, and please an old friend, which will be much better than anything Jem Fisher and little Neddy Baily will hit out for me in a week from the end of Bradshaw. I'll write to Joe, and say I'll be with him in good time on the 15th.

So I went down to the office and told Jem Fisher and little Neddy, that I had made up my mind to go and see my old friend Joe, in Berkshire, before they had had time to get their office coats on.

'What! that jolly fellow with the brown face and red whiskers,' said Jem, 'who came up and slept in your room last Christmas cattle-show, and wanted to fight the cabman for a gallon of beer, who charged him half-a-crown from Baker Street to Gray's Inn Lane?'

'Yes,' said I, 'that's the man.'

'I remember him well,' said Neddy; 'and I'm sure you'll have a good time of it if you go to see him. But, I say, how about supper tonight? You won't want us and the Bradshaws any more, eh?'

'Oh, he isn't going to get out of it like that,' said Jem, as he settled to his desk, and got his work out. 'I say, Dick, you're not going to be off now, are you? I know better.'

'I never was on that I know of,' said I; 'however, I don't mind standing supper at the Cheshire Cheese; but I won't have you fellows up in my room again tonight, kicking up a row on the stairs. No! just catch me at it!'

So I gave them supper that night, and another the night after I came back from my holiday.

They seemed just the same, but how different I felt. Only two short weeks had passed, but I was as much changed as if it had been ten years. I had found something which I never could get rid of, day or night, and which kept me always in a fret and a struggle. What a life I led with it! Sometimes it cast me down and made me ready to hang myself; and then, again, it would lift me up, and seem to fill me with warmth and sunshine. But, somehow, even when I was at the worst, if an enchanter had come and offered to wipe it all out, and to put me back just where I was the night before my holiday, I should have said 'No;' and at all other times I felt that it was the most precious part of my life. What was it? Ah, what was it? Some of you will smile, and some of you will sneer, when you find out, as you will (if you don't skip) before you get to the end of my story. And I can't see the least reason why I should help you to it a minute sooner.

CHAPTER II

OW I do pity all the lords and great gentlefolk with nothing in the world to do except to find out how to make things pleasant, and new places to go to, and new ways of spending money; at least, I always pity them at the beginning of my holiday, though perhaps when one first comes back to eleven months' hard grind in town the feeling isn't quite so strong.

At any rate, I wouldn't have changed places with the greatest lord in the land on Tuesday morning, September 15th. I was up as soon as it was light, and saw the sun rise over the Gray's Inn Lane chimney-pots; and I declare they looked quite beautiful. I didn't know at all before what a fine outline they make when the rays come flat along the roofs; and mean often to get up in time to see them by sunrise next summer; but just now it's very cold of mornings, and I dare say they don't look so well. When I put my head out of the window it was quite clear and fresh, and I thought I could smell the country.

I hadn't much to do, for I had packed my bag over night; but I went over all my things again, and changed the places of some of them in my old bureau (which belonged to my father, who was clerk for forty years in one of the oldest houses in Clement's Inn), and locked up all the drawers; and then I set to work to lay breakfast for three, for I had asked my two friends to come and see me off, and they had made it up with my landlady. So about six o'clock they came in, and we had a capital breakfast; and then we started off to walk up to the Paddington station, carrying my bag between us. I had settled to go by the 7.30 train, because if I hadn't they couldn't have come with me; besides, it is the first train which stops at Farringdon-road; and I was very glad when we got into the bustle of the station, for they were rather low, and I felt almost ashamed of being so jolly, though certainly they had had their holiday earlier in the year. But when I saw their faces out of the window of the second-class carriage, just as the starting-bell rang, I should like to have paid their fares out of my own pocket, if they could have gone with me.

However, by the time we got past Wormwood Scrubbs (which looked so fresh and breezy with the gossamer lying all over it), I could think of nothing else but the country and my holiday. How I did enjoy the pretty hill with the church at the top and the stream at the bottom by Hanwell, and the great old trees about half a mile off on the right before you get to Slough, and the view of Windsor castle, and crossing the Thames at Maidenhead, with its splendid weeping willows, and the old Bath-road bridge, and the reach beyond with the woods coming down to the bank, and the great lords' houses up above. And then all the corn-fields, though by this time were only stubble, and Reading town, and the great lasher at Pangbourn, where the water was rushing and dancing through in the sunlight to welcome me into Berkshire; and the great stretches of open land about Wallingford-road and Didcot. And after that came great green pasture-fields, and orchards, and grey-stone farmhouses, and before I could turn round we were at Farringdon-road station, and it was a quarter past eleven. As I got out and gave up my ticket, I couldn't help thinking of the two lines Jem Fisher would go on saying when we went out walking in Combe Woods and Richmond Park one Sunday this last May –

> How beautiful the country do appear
> At this time of the year.

I know he was laughing, and made them out of his own head, though he declared they were in Chaucer; but they are just as true for all that, whether Jem Fisher or Chaucer made them, though the English isn't as good as the sense.

There I found Joe waiting for me, with his trap, as he called it, at the door, and the inn ostler standing by the head of the horse, which was a bright chestnut and looked very fine. I very much enjoyed going off in that dark-green high-wheeled carriage.

'In with you, Dick,' cried out Joe, as he took hold of the reins, and patted the horse on the neck. 'There, shoot your bag in behind; look alive, she don't stand well. That'll do,' he shouted to the ostler, who jumped back and touched his hat just as if Joe owned half the parish. If the horse couldn't stand well, at any rate she could step out, and away we whirled down the white road; Joe red in the face with holding on, his feet well out to the splashboard, his chest thrown forward and his elbows down at his side, hauling the chestnut's head right back, till her nose nearly touched the collar. But for all that, away went her legs right straight out in front, shooting along so fast that I began to feel queer, not being used to horses, and took tight hold of the seat with my left hand, so that Joe shouldn't see; for the cart jumped sometimes enough to pitch you out.

'Gently there, gently, my beauty,' said Joe, as the chestnut dropped into a little quieter pace. 'There now, ain't she a pictur'?' said he to me; – 'ever see a mare lay down to her work like that? Gently, my beauty! if it wasn't for the blaze in her face, and the white feet, the Squir'd give me one hundred pounds for her tomorrow. And I won't sell her under. It's a mortal shame to drive her. Her mouth's like a kitten's.' How Joe could talk so, when he was pulling fit to burst himself at the reins, I don't know; I thought once or twice where we should go if one broke, but I didn't say anything. I found out afterwards that Joe meant a great white mark, when he talked of the blaze in her face. I suppose men can't see any faults in their own horses, any more than they can in their children.

After a bit, the pace got quietly steady, and then I began to enjoy myself, and could look at the famous rich fields, and the high hedges full of great heavy masses of clematis, and sniff up all the country smells, as we whirled along, and listen to Joe, who was going grinding on about, 'how badly the parish roads were kept up; and that he had set his mind to have them well mended with flints instead of chalk, and to have all the thistles at the side kept down, which were sowing the whole country round, because their vestry was so stingy they wouldn't put any men on the road to set it right,' and I could see that Joe was in the middle of a good quarrel with all the other farmers about it.

When he had done his story, I asked him about the White Horse, and he pointed me out the highest of the hills which ran along on our left hand a mile or two away. There, sure enough, I saw a figure quite plain; but he didn't know much about it. Only, he said, he had

always heard tell that it was cut out by King Alfred the Great, who
lived in those parts; and 'there was a main sight of strange old things
up there on the hill, besides the White Horse; and though he didn't
know much about how they got there, he was sort of proud of them,
and was glad to pay his pound or two, or double that if it was
wanted, to keep them as they should be;' 'for you see,' said Joe,
'we've lived about here, father and son, pretty nigh ever since King
Alfred's time, which I reckon is a smartish time ago, though I forget
how long.' And though I think Joe, and parties in the counties
generally, set too much store by such things, and hold their noses
much higher than they've any need to do, because their families have
never cared to move about, and push on in the world, and so they
know where their great-grandfathers were born, I couldn't help
feeling there was something in it after all.

And the more I thought of this strange old White Horse, the more
it took hold of me, and I resolved, if I could, while I was down in the
country to learn all about it. I knew, you see, that if I could only get
people to tell me about it, I should be able to carry it all away;
because, besides having a very good memory, I can take down
everything that is said as fast as most people can speak it, and that's
what gives me such an advantage over Jem Fisher and Neddy, who
spent all the time it took me to learn shorthand in reading poetry
and other rubbish, which will never help to get them on in the
world, or do them a bit of good that I can see.

Presently we came in sight of a house with farm buildings behind,
which stood some way back from the road; and Joe pulled up
opposite a gate which led into the field before the house.

'Here we are, then,' said he, 'just jump out, and open the gate,
Dick; I'd do it, only I can't trust you with the ribbons.'

It was a beautiful great green pasture-field which we drove into,
with a score of fat sleek cows feeding in it, or lying about chewing the
cud; and Joe was very proud of them, and walked the chestnut along
slowly while he pointed out his favourites to me, especially one
short-horn, whose back he said was like a kitchen-table, though why
she should be any the handsomer for that I can't say. The house was
an old brick building, with tall chimneys and latticed windows; in
front of it was a nice little flower-garden, with a tall, clipped holly
hedge running round it, so thick that you couldn't see through; and
beyond that, a kitchen-garden and an orchard. Outside the inclosure

stood four such elms as I never saw before, and a walnut-tree nearly as big as they, with queer great branches drooping close to the ground, on which some turkeys were sitting. There was only a little wicket-gate in the holly hedge, and a gravel foot-path up to the front door, so we drove into the farm-yard at the back; and while Joe and his man took care of the chestnut, I had time to look about, and think what a snug berth Joe seemed to have fallen upon.

The yard must be sixty yards across, and was full of straw where the pigs were lying with nothing but their snouts out; lots of poultry were scratching and pecking about before the barn doors, and pigeons were fluttering down amongst them, and then up again to the tops of the barns and stables, which ran all round the yard. The rick-yard, full of long stacks of hay, and round stacks of corn, was beyond. A terrier and spaniel were sleeping in sunny corners, and a greyhound was stalking about and looking at the pigs; and every-thing looked sleepy and happy, and as if life went easily at Elm Close Farm.

Presently Joe came out of the stable, carrying his whip, and took me into the house, calling into the kitchen as we passed to send in dinner directly. There was nobody in the parlour at first, but I saw that the table was laid for three; and, before I could look round at the prints and samplers on the wall, Joe's mother and the dinner came in. She was a good-looking old lady, dressed in black, with a very white lawn cap and collar, and was very kind and civil, but a little deaf. Joe bustled about, and got out I don't know how many bottles of home-made wine, clary, and raisin, and ginger; all of which he made me drink, besides beer, for he said that no one in the vale had such receipts for wine as his mother. And what with the dairy-fed pork, and black puddings, and a chicken almost as big as a turkey, and the cheesecakes and tarts afterwards, and the hearty welcome and good example which Joe gave me, I don't remember when I have made so good a dinner.

The old lady went off directly after dinner, and I could see that Joe wanted to go and see after his men; so I told him not to mind me, for I should enjoy loitering about the place better than anything. And so I did; first I went into the flower-garden, and watched and listened to the bees working away so busy in the mignonette, and the swallows darting up into their nests under the eaves, and then diving out again, and skimming away over the great pasture; and then round the kitchen-garden, and into the orchard, where the trees were all loaded with apples and pears, and so out into a stubble-field at the back, where there were a lot of young pigs feeding and playing queer tricks, and back through the farm-yard into the great pasture, where I lay down on the grass, under one of the elms, and lighted my pipe; and thought of our hot clerks' room, and how Jem Fisher and little Neddy were working away there; and watched a flock of little shiny starlings hopping up on the backs of some old south-down wethers who were feeding near me, and flying backwards and forwards into the old elms and walnut trees, talking to one another all the while.

And so the time wore on, till a stout lass in a blue cotton print came out, and called the cows in to milking; and they all went trooping slowly by into the farmyard, some of them just stopping to stare at me with their mild eyes, and smelling so sweet, that I hadn't the heart to go on smoking, and let my pipe out. And after a bit I followed into the line of sheds where they were being milked by the lass and a man, who balanced himself on two legs of the milking-stool, and drove his head into the cow's side; and I thought I had never heard a sweeter sound than the tinkling sound which the milk made in the bright tin pails.

I soon got into a talk with the lass, who was very pleasant and free spoken; and presently, when her pail was full, I lifted it out for her, all frothing up, and looking not a bit like our London sky-blue; and I told her I didn't think I had ever tasted real new milk; so she got me a long straw, and while she went on milking, I went down on my knees, and began to suck away through the straw. But I had hardly begun, when I heard a noise behind, and looking round, there stood Joe, laughing all over; and by his side a young woman in a broad straw hat and a grey jacket; and though, for good manners, she didn't laugh out like Joe, I could see it was all she could do to keep from going off too.

Why was I ashamed of being caught? I don't know, but I was ashamed; and as I stuck there on my knees in the deep straw with the pail before me looking at them, the blood rushed up to my head and made my ears sing, so that I couldn't hear a word that Joe said. But I could see he did say something, and then went off into another great roar of laughter; and the lass and the man left off milking and began laughing too, till I thought they would have dropped the stools.

Then the young woman who was with Joe said something to him, and I thought I heard the words 'What a shame!' and 'your oldest friend;' and then she caught up a straw, and came and knelt on the opposite side of the milk-pail, and begun sucking away herself without looking at me. In another moment Joe plumped down too, clapping me on the back.

'I say,' said he, 'start fair! Here, make room for me; you and Lucy ain't going to have it all to yourselves,' and he began sucking away too; and then I recovered myself, and we all went on for a minute, when Joe took his straw out of his mouth, and said, 'This is my sister Lucy, Dick; there, shake hands over the pail, and then let's go in to tea.'

So she looked up, and blushed, and gave me her hand, her merry blue eyes twinkling with mirth, though she tried to keep grave. But I was all right now, and went off myself, and Joe followed, and then she, with the clearest, brightest laugh you ever heard; and then the man and the lass, and by the time we had done, I felt as if I had known them all for years. But as for Miss Lucy, as we walked away to the house to tea, I felt as if I could have given her my skin, if she would only have had a pair of shoes made out of it for her dear little feet.

The old lady was sitting at the tea-table in great force, with plates of buttered toast and cake, and pots of blackberry and redcurrant jam, and the great loaf all set out ready; and after tea we three walked out again till the sun set, and then came in to supper, at which I was suprised to find myself eating away just as if I had had nothing all day; country air does give one such an appetite. After supper the old lady sat in her chair knitting and telling stories, till she nodded off and the spectacles fell on to the end of her nose, and her hands in her lap, but still holding the needles; and every now and then giving a catch with her head, and making belief to go on for a stitch or two. And Miss Lucy sat stitching at a patch-work coverlet, fitting in all sorts of scraps of silk in the prettiest patterns in the world, and we on the other side of the table watching her, and talking quite low not to disturb the old lady. But what made it so pleasant was, that I had pretty near all the talking, for they seemed never tired of hearing about London, and how people lived there, and what they thought; especially Miss Lucy, who had never been out of Berkshire in her life. I thought Joe a great fidget, when soon after nine he began to walk about and waked his mother, and got the servants in to prayers and bustled them off to bed: but I believe it was all because he wanted to have his pipe, which he wouldn't smoke in the parlour. So he went into the kitchen and finished the day there, under half a score of great brown sides of bacon, and tufts of sweet herbs which hang drying from the corners of the rack, and opposite to the dresser with its rows of pewter plates as bright as silver, till I went to bed in sheets smelling of lavender, and dreamt of Miss Lucy.

I dare say that, though I should never be tired of telling about everything that happened to me at Elm Close, some people may get tired of reading about it. So I shall only begin my story of the next day after breakfast, when Joe had the trap out again, and carried me off to see what was doing up on White Horse Hill.

We had a very pleasant drive through the Vale of Uffington, which lies at the foot of the hill, and here Joe put up the trap, at the Swan, and we set off on foot to walk up. It was very hot, and the white road glared as we tramped along it, but very soon we came to broad strips of turf on each side, and then it was pleasant enough; so we plodded up a gentle rise called Sour Hill, and crossed the Iceldon or Iggleton way, which I've found out since was an old Roman road; and then the ascent became quite steep, and everything was clear hill and down before us, not a fence to be seen, and a fresh breeze came sweeping over the hill.

The road now became very bad, with ruts in the chalk like water-courses. On our left hand there was a deep narrow valley like a little bay running up into the hill, on the opposite side of which valley a large wood hung along the steepest part of the hillside, which Joe informed me was Uffington wood, a well-known meet for the hounds: it made me giddy to look at the places which he declared the huntsman, and any one who wanted to be sure of a good place when the hounds broke cover, had to ride along.

And now the great green hill seemed to be hanging right over us, as we came to a curious round mound on our right hand, up which Joe scrambled, and I after him, till we both pulled up out of breath on the flat top some fifty yards across.

'This is Dragon's Hill,' said Joe, pulling off his hat and mopping his face with his handkerchief, 'where St George killed the Dragon in the old times. Leastways so they says about here, only they calls him King George instead of Saint George. And this bare place is where his blood ran out, and nothing'll grow on it since, not so much as a thistle.'

Of course I knew better than to believe that, but it is a beautiful place: for just below it another little deep valley, like the one on the left, only narrower and steeper at the sides, runs right up into the hill-side. The road we had left winds round the head of this gorge, for any one to drive along who isn't particular about breaking his neck, for the hill is like a wall up above, and down below, with nothing but a little bank between you and the descent.

'Those are the giants' seats opposite,' said Joe, pointing across the valley to a set of beautiful great green slopes, like huge ridges and furrows, which were sweeping down into the valley one after another as far as I could see; 'and this is the Manger, this great hole in the hill-side, because it lies right under the old Horse's nose. Come along, let's get up to him; there he is, you see, right above us.'

So we scrambled down the side of Dragon's Hill, crossed the road, and then started up a row of steps cut in the turf. I'm sure it must be twice as steep as the hill in Greenwich Park, and I don't mind confessing that I shouldn't have liked to look round just at first, and wouldn't have minded giving myself a help with my hands if I hadn't been afraid of Joe's seeing me and laughing. I should think we must have gone up two hundred steps, when all of a sudden Joe stopped just above me, and called out, 'Here we are;' and in about four steps I came to a trench cut into the chalk about two feet deep, which ran up the hill-side right ahead of us. The chalk in the trench was all hard and flat, and seemed to have been scraped and brushed up quite lately.

'This is his tail,' said Joe. 'Come on; look, they're scouring him up above; we're in luck – I thought they'd have done before this; and there's the Squire too with 'em.'

So I looked up; and there, some way above, I saw a lot of men with shovels, and besoms, and barrows, cleaning away at the trench, which, now that I began to look at it, certainly came out more and more like a horse galloping; and there amongst them, working away as hard as any one, was a person in yellow leather gaiters, who I saw at once must be the Squire, though I had never seen a squire before. I own I had a great prejudice against a country squire when I went down into Berkshire; which was natural enough, you, see, because I had never been farther from town than Twickenham (except by boat to Margate), and had belonged to a debating society near Farringdon-market ever since I left school, where we take in three liberal papers, and once a week have as good speaking as they get in the House of Commons. I haven't been to the debates much lately, myself; but when I was an active member, we used to have regular go in about once a quarter at the unpaid magistracy. How we did give it them! They were bloated aristocrats, who by the time they were thirty had drunk out all the little brains they ever had, and spent their time in preserving and killing game and foxes at the expense of the farmers, and sending every good man in their villages either to the Bastile (as we called the workhouse) as a pauper, or to the county gaol as a poacher.

Joe and I very nearly quarrelled over one of those debates to which I took him, like a great gaby as I was, when he came up to see me at the time of a cattle-show. He would get up to speak, all I could do to stop him; and began, all red in the face, pitching into one of our best speakers who had just finished, calling him a cockney, and asking him what right he had to jaw about squires when he talked about a fox's ears and tail, and didn't know mangold-wurzel from swedes. And then all our fellows began to shout and hiss, and Joe began to swear, and wanted to take his coat off, and fight all who had spoken, 'one down, and t'other come on,' as he said. I got him out and took him home; but his blood was up, and he would go on at our Society, and call us a set of quill-driving jackanapes. And I couldn't stand that, so I began at the landed interest, and said all the bad of them I could think of, about the Poor-laws, game preserving, and Corn-laws. Joe was very near going off in a huff, but we shook hands it at last, and agreed that we neither of us knew much about the sort of life the other led, and so had better not talk about it as if we did.

Well, this was the first squire I had ever seen, so I looked at him with all my eyes; and if all squires were like him, I don't wonder at Joe's getting in a passion at our talk in Farringdon-market. I should think he must be about forty-five years old, and stands not far short of six feet high; for when he came to stand by Joe, I could see he was the taller of the two; but he didn't look so tall quite when he stood by himself – I suppose because his figure was so good. For you never saw such a clean made man; he was for all the world like a well-rounded wedge from his shoulders down, and his neck and head put on like a statue. He looked as if he could have jumped the highest five-barred gate in the vale, and then have carried it off on his shoulders, and run up the hill with it. And his face, which was well browned, was so manly and frank, and his voice was so cheery, and he looked you so straight in the face, that you felt he wasn't ashamed of anything, or afraid of anybody; and so you looked him back and spoke out, and were twice as good a man at once yourself while you were talking to him.

Well, when the Squire saw Joe, he stopped working away with his shovel, and called out to him; and so Joe went up and shook hands with him, and began talking to him, and in another minute the Squire called for his coat – a grey tweed shooting-jacket it was – and put it on, and took up his riding-whip, and told the men to look alive and get their job done, and then to send up to the Castle for some beer and bread and cheese which he would order for them.

Then Joe and the Squire walked away along the hill-side talking, and I went and sat down on a little mound, just above the Horse's ears, and watched the men working, and looked at the view. How I did enjoy myself! The turf was as soft as a feather-bed, and as springy as horse-hair; and it was all covered with thistle-down, which came drifting along like snow with the south wind; and all down below the country looked so rich and peaceful, stretching out for miles and miles at my feet in the hazy sunshine, and the larks right up overhead sang so sweetly, that I didn't know whether to laugh or cry. I should have liked to have had a turn at the besoms and shovels with the men, who seemed very good-tempered, only I was too shy, and I couldn't make out half they said. So I took out my pipe and lighted it, and sat looking on at the work, and thinking of nothing.

Presently a gentleman whom I hadn't noticed, but who was poking about the place, came and sat down near me. He was dressed in dark clothes, very quiet; I suppose he was a parson from some of the villages near. And we began talking about the weather, and what chance there was of having fine days for the pastime. He was a very grave, elderly man, but easy and pleasant, and had a keen look in his grey eyes, and a sort of twinkle about his mouth, which made me put my best leg fore most, and take care what I said.

Well, when we had done about the weather, thinks I, 'This is just the sort of gentleman to tell me what I want to know about the White Horse and all the rest of it,' and you'll see as you go on that I never made a better guess in my life. So I got my note-book out quietly, so that he shouldn't take much notice of what I was about, and began, 'I suppose, Sir,' said I, 'that its all right about Alfred, and that he really did cut out this figure after winning a great battle up here?'

'Yes,' said he, 'I think so myself, because there had always been a tradition in the country side that this was so. And where antiquaries differ, a tradition of this sort may always be pretty safely believed. Country folk hold on to such stories, and hand them down in a very curious manner; but you know, I dare say, that it is claimed by some as a Druidical, or at any rate a British monument, which would make it several hundred years older at least.'

I didn't know anything about it, but why should I tell him so. 'I shouldn't like to think so, Sir,' said I, 'because one wouldn't care so much about it if it wasn't made by the Saxons and their great king. The Druids don't seem akin to us somehow; and then one would lose all about the great battle, which was certainly fought up here, wasn't it, Sir?'

'I have no doubt about it,' said he; 'there are many signs of it –
above all, graves enough to hold the harvest of many battles. You are
lying on one.'

'No! am I really, though?' said I, sitting up and looking at the
ground; 'how do you know?'

'Well, it isn't very hard when the eye gets used to them,' said he:
'there's another;' and he pointed to a small mound a few yards off,
and just like, the one I was sitting on. 'That larger mound, too,
down below, across the road, you were on it just now –'

'Yes, Sir,' said I, interrupting him, and pointing at it, 'Dragon's
Hill.'

'Exactly so,' said he; 'that's another burial-place; a larger and
grander affair, you see, than these. Probably a king or other very
notable person is buried there.'

'The people say, Sir, don't they,' said I, 'that St George killed the
Dragon there?'

'They do,' said he, 'and that his blood made a pool on the top, and
ran down the steps on the other side, where the grass has never
grown since. This is another curious instance of the tenacity of

tradition; but here I think our good folk in the Vale have held on to
the name, or a part of it, and forgotten the meaning, just as they have
in the case of another village over there in Oxfordshire, the name of
which is Stanton Harcourt.'

'How was that, Sir?' said I, when he paused.

'Well,' said he, laughing, 'an old man in that village told me that a
battle was fought there, which the English were very near losing,
when the general rode up to one of his captains, named Harcourt,
who was in the thick of it, and called out, "Stan' to un, Harcourt,
stan' to un, Harcourt;" and that Harcourt won the battle, and the
village has been called Stanton Harcourt ever since. Now, as to that
mound, I believe it's right name to be Pendragon's Hill. Pendragon,
you know, is only a name common to those of the kings of the
ancient Britons, who were chosen leaders in the time of national
distress, and means nothing more than "caput regum," "the chief of
kings." According to some, "Arthur" is the same or a like word,
being "Ardh-reg" or "Ard-heer," and meaning "summus Rex"
(whence the "Arviragus" of Juvenal; but I lay no stress on this).
Now we know of at least three Pendragons. There was Cassibelan,
who was chosen Pendragon at the time of Julius Caesar's invasion,
Uter Pendragon, and Arthur Pendragon; which Uter and Arthur
were, without doubt, chosen to resist the Saxons, who had won
already the eastern part of the island. And if Arthur and Pendragon
are the same words, doubtless (as has been well supposed) there
were many Arthurs at this time, one of whom was probably slain in
battle and buried here.[1] For in the Saxon annals we find that Cedric,
founder of the West Saxon kingdom, slew Natan-leod and five
thousand men in these parts, which Natan-leod (as is shown by Mr
Baxter) is "Naud-an-ludh," or "populi tutela," the people's refuge; in
fact, a kindred word to "Pendragon," or "Arthur." You see how
probable this would be *prima facia?*' said he, turning round to me.

My goodness! I couldn't make out head or tail of all his long
words, and was staring at him with my mouth open; but when he
turned round I shut it pretty quick, and looked as wise as I could.
'Well, Sir,' said I, 'I hardly know; but it doesn't look unlikely, does
it?'

'Of course not,' said he, quite pleased; 'and as the Britons were not
driven from these parts till the middle of the sixth century, I should
put the throwing up of Dragon's Hill in the beginning, say the first

half, of that century. Now, in the year AD 520, according to Gildas and Bede, Arthur gained his twelfth victory at "Mons Badonicus," which might very well be Baydon Hill, which you see over there.' And he pointed to a hill three or four miles off.

'But then, Sir,' said I, 'if he gained the victory, he wasn't killed there, I suppose, and so he couldn't be buried here.'

'But he was killed in battle at last,' said he; 'and as I told you, there must have been many Arthurs or Pendragons just at that time, and many battles fought between this and Bath – why, the Britons gained a battle at Wanborough, over there, as late as AD 581.'

'But, Sir,' said I, 'if Pendragon was buried down there, wouldn't they have been very likely to cut out the horse up here just above, as another monument, at the same time; and then what becomes of King Alfred and the Danes?'

'There is no instance of two such monuments over one chief,' answered he, quite positive; but I thought I saw him give a twinkle with his mouth, as if he felt I had been pretty near him. 'Besides, as I said before, the tradition as to the White Horse is too strong to be upset by conjecture.'

'I didn't mean to conjecture, I'm sure, Sir,' said I; and I thought, though I didn't say so, it was he who had been conjecturing pretty freely, if it came to that. 'The battle of Ashdown, Sir, was a very great battle then,' I went on, for I liked to hear him talk about those old times, though I didn't quite understand all he said.

'The greatest battle probably in which Alfred ever was,' said he.

'Please, Sir,' said I, 'I hope you won't think me troublesome, but if you would only tell me about the battle I should be so much obliged to you.'

'Sir,' said he, looking at me rather surprised, 'it is seldom that I can get any of the youth of this day to take an interest in these matters, the study of which would greatly benefit their manners and morals. I shall be pleased to do what you wish. Are you a good listener?'

'Yes, Sir,' said I, 'you will get tired of talking long before I shall of listening. And you wouldn't mind, I hope, my taking notes of the story?'

'By no means,' said he; 'I see you are ready with your pen. Perhaps I shouldn't have told you so much about Pendragon and Natan-leod if I had seen that you were taking me down; but now I will be careful to give you nothing which is not to be found in the most trustworthy chroniclers. Are you ready?'

'Yes, Sir,' said I; and then he settled himself in the turf, and pulled a couple of old brown books out of his long coat-tail pockets, to which he sometimes referred, and looking out over the vale, as if he were travelling in his mind far away from me and everything about us on the hill-side, began as follows.

NOTES

1.   E. Martin Atkins, Esq., of Kingston Lisle, has lately been opening the barrows which are nearest to the Horse; and the compiler hearing that he was about to examine Dragon's Hill also wrote to him on the subject, and suggested how desirable it would be (if any ways possible) to find the remains of King Bægseek there, who was slain at Ashdown. To which communication the compiler received the following reply. After mentioning the contents of the other barrows, some clearly Saxon, others Romano-British, his letter proceeds as to Dragon's Hill:–

'As for old Bægseek, I should chuck him overboard at once, and assume that our friend Uter Pendragon's remains had been originally deposited here, but that he had been disturbed in his repose by the decapitation of the barrow, which at some unknown time has undoubtedly taken place. It is unfortunate, however, that a Roman coin of the time of Constans turned up from among the debris, and the fragments of pottery also were chiefly of Roman manufacture, mixed with some of earlier date. It will therefore perhaps be difficult to reconcile these matters one with the other; but on turning them over in your mind, you will, I dare say, *theorise with a very agreeable correctness!*' What is a wretched compiler to do, who gets such letter from those who should be his aiders and abettors?

CHAPTER III

EARLY a thousand years ago, in the year of our Lord 871, the great battle of Ashdown was fought; but, in order to give you a true idea of its importance, I must begin my story some years earlier; that is to say, in the year of our Lord 866. In this year, Æthelbert, king of the West Saxons, died, having ruled his kingdom for five years in peace, with the love of his subjects; and Æthelred, his next brother, who succeeded him, buried his body in Sherborne Minster. In this year Alfred, the younger brother, who afterwards succeeded Æthelred, and was called Alfred the Great, reached his seventeenth year. In the autumn a great army of pagan Danes came over to Britain, and landed in that part of the island which was then called East Anglia, but now Norfolk. These were not the first Danes who had come over to vex England, but none of them ever stayed so long, fought so many battles, or did so much harm (as we should say, speaking according to man's judgement) as these.

A very curious story is told of why they came over here; and as it goes at first sight against a good many of our notions of how the world is governed, and so ought to make us think a little more about the matter, I shall give it you pretty much as it is told by the old chronicler John Brompton.

'There was a man of royal birth in the kingdom of Denmark named Lodbroc, who had two sons, Hinguar and Hubba. This man embarked one day with his hawk in a small boat to catch ducks, and other wildfowl on the adjoining sea-coasts and islands. A terrible storm arose, by which Lodbroc was carried away and tossed for several days on every part of the ocean. After numberless perils, he was cast ashore on the coast of Norfolk, near the village of Redham,' (at least that must be the name as I read it in Brompton, though I have not been able to hear of a village of that name on the coast of Norfolk,) 'where he was found having his hawk alone for his companion, and presented to King Edmund. That king, struck with the manliness of his form, kept him at his court and heard from his own mouth the history of his adventures. He was then associated with Berne, the king's huntsman, and indulged in all the pleasures of the chase, for in the exercise of both hunting and hawking he was remarkably skilful, and succeeded in capturing both birds and beasts according as he had a mind.' In fact, Lodbroc was the sort of man to please King Edmund, for the art of capturing birds and beasts was, next to the art of fighting for one's home and country, the art most esteemed amongst the Anglo-Saxons; who acknowledged 'that skill and good fortune in this art, as in all others, are among the gifts of God, as we also have often witnessed.' But to go on with our story. 'The skill of Lodbroc bred jealousy in the heart of Berne the huntsman, who one day, as they went out together hunting,

unawares set upon Lodbroc, and having foully slain him, buried his body in the thickets of the forest. But Lodbroc had a small harrier dog, which he had bred up from its birth, and which loved him much. While Berne the huntsman went home with the other hounds, this little dog remained alone with his master's body. In the morning the king asked what had become of Lodbroc, to which Berne answered that he had parted from him yesterday in the woods, and had not seen him since. At that moment the harrier came into the hall and went round wagging its tail, and fawning on the whole company, but especially on the king; when he had eaten his fill, he again left the hall. This happened often; until someone at last followed the dog to see where he went, and having found the body of the murdered Lodbroc, came and told the story to the king. The affair was now carefully inquired into, and when the truth was at last found out, the huntsman was exposed on the sea, without oars, in the boat which had belonged to Lodbroc. In some days he was cast ashore in Denmark, and brought before the sons of Lodbroc: who, putting him to the torture, inquired of him what had become of their father, to whom they knew the boat belonged. To this Berne answered,' as one might have guessed he would answer, he being a liar and cowardly murderer, 'that their father Lodbroc had fallen into the hands of Edmund, King of East Anglia, by whose orders he had been put to death.' Now King Edmund was a wise and righteous man, who 'devoutly undertook the government of the East Angles, and held it with the right hand of power, always adoring and glorifying God for all the good things which he enjoyed;' [1] and it is a pity he did not on this occasion remember that having safely caught a great scoundrel, the best thing to do with him was to see him hung out of the way himself; for by letting him go, you see, he gave a chance to the devil, who can't afford to lose such gentleman as Berne the huntsman out of the world, and has considerable grudges against kings like Edmund.

Well, when Hinguar and Hubba heard the tale of Berne the huntsman, they, like good and true sons, according to the notions of piety then current amongst the Danes, hastened to fit out a fleet to invade England and avenge their father. And their three sisters wove for them the standard called the Raven in one day – which flag waved over many a bloody field, from Northumbria to Devonshire, until it was taken by King Alfred's men, under Odda the Alderman of Devon, before a certain castle in that country, which is called Cynuit by Asser, and Kenuith elsewhere (the situation of which castle I cannot identify, or the name), where were slain King Halfdene, a brother of Hinguar and Hubba, and 840 Danish warriors. It was said, that when the Danes were about to gain a battle, a live crow would fly before the middle of the standard; but if they were to be beaten, it would hang motionless.[2]

So Hinguar and Hubba, as has been said, landed in the country of the East Angles, in the late autumn, bent on vengeance. King Edmund knew nothing of the blood-feud between him and these Danish leaders, by reason of Berne's lying story, so took no more notice than the usual measures for preparing to attack them; but whether it was that they found King Edmund too strong for them at the time, or for some other reason, they seem to have wintered there quietly, and to have bought horses, and made some sort of truce with the East Angles.[3] But in the spring of the year 867 they crossed the Humber, marched hastily upon York, and took it.

The kingdom of Northumbria was just the place for the army of Pagans and the standard Raven at this time; for it was divided against itself. Osbert, the rightful king, had been playing Tarquin in the house of Bruern Brocard, one his chief earls: so his people had cast him out, and had taken to themselves a king Ælla, of unkingly blood, and the two were warring against one another when the Danes took York. Late in the autumn, however, a peace was made between Osbert and Ælla, and they marched to York; where within the very walls of the city into which the Northumbrians penetrated, was fought a most bloody battle. In that fight fell almost all the Northumbrian warriors, and both the kings, and a multitude of noble men; and the remainder who escaped made peace with the Pagans.[4] By this time, no doubt, there was small spoil left for Hinguar and Hubba north of the Humber.

Accordingly, in the year 868, the pagan army, leaving Northumbria, marched into Mercia, and surprised and took Nottingham. Then Burhred, King of Mercia, and his witan sent to Æthelred, king of the West Saxons, to come and help them. And Æthelred and Alfred marched to Nottingham with the West Saxon power, and with Burhred besieged the Pagans there; but they could not force the wall, and there was no great battle, and Æthelred and Alfred went home with their troops. But the Pagans, after wintering at Nottingham, made peace with Burhred and the Mercians; that is to say, such a peace as they loved to make – I mean a peace till it was worth their while to come again; for in 874 they came back, drove King Burhred over the sea, and subdued the whole country – and Burhred went to Rome and died there, and his body lies in St Mary's Church at the English School.[5]

In the year 869, 'the aforesaid army of Pagans, galloping back to Northumbria, went to York, and there passed winter;' or, in the words of Huntingdon, 'remained there cruelly for one year.' And what sort of a winter was it for the poor Yorkshiremen? 'There was again a great famine, a mortality among men, and a pest among cattle.' Such is the fate of a divided people which can only make truces with its oppressors.

In this winter, Hinguar and Hubba seem to have got large reinforcements from over the sea, headed by two other kings, Bægseeg and Halfdane their brother, for in the year 870 we find them no longer surprising a city, and from thence defying their enemies and oppressing the neighbourhood. Now they march very openly and fearlessly across Mercia: and, the day of vengeance having come, burst upon East Anglia, and take up their head-quarters at Thetford. And then comes the saddest part of a sad story. King Edmund, being a king like Josiah, who believed in God and ruled in righteousness, was not the man to see the desolation of any part of his people, or to shut himself up in fenced cities while the pagan cavalry rode through East Anglia – so the aforesaid King Edmund gathered his men, and 'fought fiercely and manfully against the army. But because the merciful God foreknew that he was to arrive at the crown of martyrdom, he there fell gloriously. Of his passion I would fain insert some particulars into our history, that the sons of men may know and perceive how terrible is Christ the Son of God in the counsels of men, and with what glorious triumph He adorns those whom He tries here under the name of suffering, that the saying may be fulfilled, "He is not crowned except he strive lawfully." (2 Tim.ii.5.)'[6] Such is the lesson which the old monk Simeon, præcentor of the Church of Durham, gets out of the death and martyrdom of King Edmund, and I know not where we are to look for a better. Perhaps it may help us when we think of India[7] to remember with Simeon, how terrible is Christ the Son of God in the counsels of men, and with what glorious triumph He adorns those whom he tries here under the name of suffering. For Hinguar and Hubba took the wounded king on the field of battle, and tied him to a tree, because he chose to die sooner than give over his people to them, and there shot him through the body with their arrows.[8] But his people got the body and buried it at Bradoriesunyrthe, now

called St Edmund's Bury, or Bury St Edmunds;[9] and many friends were wrought at his tomb, and he was canonized – at which honour let all Englishmen rejoice, the earth having as much need as ever of many such kings and saints.

And they were rare then as now, and then as now men went their own way, and not God's way, and cut out their own work instead of taking His. For 'when King Edmund was slain, his brother Edwold, dreading the pleasures of the world, and seeing that a hard lot had fallen in himself and his brother, retired to the monastery of Carnelia in Dorsetshire, near a clear well which St Augustine had formerly brought out of the earth by prayer, to baptize the people in, and there he led a hermit's life on only bread and water.'[10] Yes! and no doubt thought himself righteous and despised others – and left the kingdom which God had given him to the Pagans, who, 'subdued all the land and destroyed all the minsters they came to,' which Edmund his brother had built – 'and that same time they came to Medeshamstede, and burned and beat it down, slew abbot and monks, and all that place which before was full rich they reduced to nothing,'[11] while Edwold, who should have been there with the remnant of the East Angles, to make his last stand, like a true shepherd of his people, was eating his bread and drinking his water in peace, by a clear well near the monastery of Carnelia in Dorsetshire.

And now the Pagan kings, 'with a new army, very great, like a flowing river which carries all along with it,'[12] having doubtless been reinforced again from over the sea, where the story of their victories had spread far and wide, were looking about for some new field for plunder and murder. The whole north and east of England was a desolate wilderness behind them; London was in ruins, and Kent had been harried over and over again by their brethren the sea-kings. But some thirty miles up the Thames was a fair kingdom, stretching far away west, down to the district sea. This was Wessex, the kingdom of the West Angles, over which Æthelred, the brother of Alfred, was now ruling, and entering on the sixth year of his reign. The kingdom had had peace for ten years, and was full of royal burgs, and rich pastures, with cattle, and horses, and sheep. Perhaps Hinguar and Hubba remembered the leaguer of Nottingham three years before, and how the West Angles, with their king and his brother, had hemmed them in and watched them there through a long summer.

In the early years of their inroad, the Pagans would not have dared to brave a united people with Æthelred for king; but they had now grown bold from success, and were in numbers so great that 'by reason thereof they could not advance together, but went by different roads.' So in an early month of the year 871, with their usual swiftness they marched up the Thames valley and seized on Reading, a royal burg, and the then eastern-most city of note in Wessex. Reading is situated on the south bank of the Thames and on the north bank of the Kennet, at the confluence of the two rivers; and, while part of the Pagan host made a rampart between the rivers, to protect their camp and the town which they had taken, a large force, on the third day after their arrival, began scouring the country for plunder, under two of their earls.

But the men of Wessex had increased and multiplied as well as their cattle, and Æthelwulf, Alderman of Berkshire, was a man 'who rages as a lion in battle.' So Aethelwulf, with what men he could get together, fought with the two earls at Englefield, though he had but a small band of Christians with him. But he cheered his men, saying to them, 'though they attack us with the advantage of more men we may despise them, for our commander Christ is braver than they.'[13] Whereupon the men of Wessex buckled to their work under the oaks of Englefield Chase (afterwards beloved by the great Queen Bess), and there discomfited the pagans very sore, and slew one of the two earls. In one of the old chroniclers, there are a few lines which may partly account for Æthelwulf's victory; 'their two consuls,' says Æthelwerd, 'forgetting that they were not on board their fleet, rode proudly through fields and meadows on horseback, which nature had denied them;' possibly therefore these were the newcomers, who had just joined the Pagan army, and were not used to horses or land-fighting.

Within the next three days King Æthelred and his brother Alfred came up from the west, each leading a strong band of West Saxon warriors, and joined Æthelwulf; and on the fourth day they attacked the Pagans at Reading. Those who were outside the rampart they cut to pieces, and at first had the vantage; but the Pagans came out with all their forces, and after great slaughter had been made on either hand, and the brave Æthelwulf had been slain, 'the Pagans had possession of the place of death.'[14] Thus the chronicle states it; probably the men of Wessex were grievously beaten, and went back with their king, in confusion, along the chalk hills to the other end of Berkshire, pursued by Bægseeg and Halfdene, the two lately arrived Danish kings, with the strength of the Pagan host. I suppose that Hinguar and Hubba stayed at Reading, to hold the place of safety; for neither of them were at Ashdown.

But every mile as they fell back added strength to Æthelred and Alfred, as bands of men came up from the rear; from the broad Wiltshire plains over the Kennet at Hungerford, and along the chalk hills from Swindon and Ashbury; from the vales of the Kennet and the Thames on either flank; and a few perhaps already from Glostershire and Oxfordshire, where the news was doubtless spreading like the wind. So Æthelred and his host turned to bay at Ashdown, and set the battle in array against the pagan kings.

There is some question between antiquaries as to where the exact site of this battle is. It must however, it seems to me, be somewhere in the western part of Berkshire; for it is quite impossible that Æthelred and Alfred could have fought at Reading, at Ashdown, and at Basing, as they unquestionably did, within three weeks, if we are to look for Ashdown battle-field either at Ashdown forest, in Essex, or at Ashendon, in the hundred of Bernwood in Buckinghamshire, which are the only sites out of Berkshire claiming this honour, and supported by a title of authority. Besides, even supposing these three battles could have been fought in the time, yet the battle of Reading having gone against the Saxons (as to which every chronicler agrees), is it likely that they should have retired *past* the town and stronghold of the Danes, either north-east into Buckinghamshire, or south-east into Sussex, leaving the whole of Wessex open to the enemy, instead of falling back westward into Wessex, and so covering their own homes? It is perfectly absurd to suppose this, Alfred being one of their generals; and how such ancient and venerable persons as Bishops Kennet and Leland can have talked such nonsense, is hard to say; unless indeed they were born, the one in Sussex, the other in Buckinghamshire, in which case it is of course excusable, nay, justifiable in them; but of this I know nothing.

As to the Berkshire sites I don't see any reason for troubling you with their several titles. I am myself satisfied that the battle was fought here; but all the sites are somewhere on this range of chalk hills, of which the old White Horse is king. So now we will turn to the account of the great battle in the old chroniclers.

'About four days after the battle at Reading, King Æthelred and Alfred his brother fought against the whole army of the Pagans at Ashdown. And they were in two bodies; in the one were Bægseeg and Halfdene the Pagan kings, and in the other were the earls.' 'Now the Christians had determined that King Æthelred with his men should attack the two Pagan kings, but that Alfred his brother with his men

should take the chance of war against the earls. Things being so
settled, the king remained a long time in prayer, hearing the mass,
and said he would not leave it till the priest had done, nor abandon
the protection of God for that of men. And so he did, which
afterwards availed him much with the Almighty, as we shall declare
more fully in the sequel. But the Pagans came up quickly to the
fight. Then Alfred, though holding a lower authority, as I have been
told by those who were there and would not lie, could no longer
support the troops without waiting for his brother: so he marched
out promptly with his men in a close column and gave battle.' 'He
too,' as Simeon says, 'knowing without a doubt that victory would
not lie with a multitude of men, but in the pity and mercy of God,'
and seeing also that, mass or no mass, the Pagans must not be
allowed to get between him and his brother. 'But here I must inform
those who are ignorant of the fact, that the field of battle was not
equal for both armies. The Pagans occupied the higher ground, and
the Christians came up from below. There was also in that place a
single stunted thorn-tree, which I myself have seen with my own
eyes. Around this tree the opposing hosts came together with loud
shouts from all sides, the one to pursue their wicked course, the
other to fight for their lives, their dearest ties, and their country.' 'In
the midst of the fight, and when Alfred was hard pressed,' –
according to Brompton, for the older chroniclers do not mention
this, – 'the king came up with his fresh forces.' 'And when both hosts
had fought long and bravely, at last the Pagans, by God's judgement, could no longer bear the attack of the Christians, and having
lost great part of their men, took to a disgraceful fight, and all the
Pagan host pursued its flight not only until night, but the next day,
even until they reached the stronghold from which they had come
out. The Christians followed, slaying all they could reach, until it
became dark.'[15] 'And the flower of the Pagan youth were there slain,
so that neither before nor since was ever such destruction known
since the Saxons first gained Britain by their arms.' 'There fell in
that battle King Bægseeg and these earls with him; that old Earl
Sidroc, to whom may be applied that ancient saying "the ancient of
evil days," and Earl Sidroc the younger, and Earl Osbern, and Earl
Frœna, and Earl Harold; who, with their men, choosing the broad
and spacious way, went down into the depths of the lake;' or, let us
perhaps hope not, old monk Simeon, seeing that they died gallantly

in harness, and that, as you yourself add in the next sentence, 'they knew not the way of teaching nor understood its paths; it was kept far away from their faces.' It is fair to add that Brompton states that Æthelred slew Bægseeg with his spear, and another Pagan of note with his sword after he got up to the fight; but the older chroniclers do not mention this.[16]

To finish briefly the history of the rest of the year 871, fourteen days after the battle of Ashdown, Æthelred and Alfred fought another battle with the Pagans (probably with that part which had remained in garrison at Reading, with Hinguar and Hubba, and the relics of Halfdene's army) at Basing, which seems to have been undecided; and two months afterwards another at Merton. After which, in the summer, reinforcements came from beyond sea, and joined the Pagans; King Æthelred died, and Alfred fought before the winter four more pitched battles. So, as the Saxon Chronicle sums up, 'in this year nine general battles were fought against the army in the kingdom south of the Thames: besides which, Alfred, the king's brother, and single aldermen and king's thanes, oftentimes made attacks on them which were not numbered, and slew of them within the year one king and nine earls.' This was not what the Pagans reckoned on: they liked fighting very much in reason, as an accompaniment of spoiling a country, and did it well; but to be fighting nine pitched battles in a year, hemmed-in in one corner of a rich kingdom (for they never got farther than a few miles into Wiltshire), and getting no spoil even there, was not to their taste; so in the winter they made truce with Alfred, and took themselves off to their old haunts in Mercia and Northumbria, and did not return for five years.

This year, AD 871, is a year for Berkshire men to be proud of, for on them fell the brunt of that fiery trial; and their gallant stand probably saved England a hundred years of Paganism. For had they given way to Ashdown, and the reinforcements from over the sea come to a conquering instead of to a beaten army in the summer, there was nothing to stop the Pagans between Reading and Exeter. The other eight battles were skirmishes in comparison with this one: they scarcely occupy five lines each in the chroniclers, and out of the king and nine Pagan earls who were slain within the year, six fell at Ashdown. It was Alfred's crowning mercy; and so he felt it to be, and in memory of it he caused his army (tradition says, on the day after the battle) to carve the White Horse, the standard of Hengist, on the hill-side just under the Castle, where it stands as you see until this day.

'Thank you, Sir,' said I, when he paused, 'what a grand story it makes! And are those the real words of the old chroniclers, as you call them, Sir, which you used?'

'Yes,' said he, 'almost every word is simply a translation from one or other of them, but the greater part is taken from the Chronicle of Asser, who was a contemporary and intimate friend of Alfred, and a very learned and pious ecclesiastic.'

'I suppose they were mostly priests and monks who wrote the Chronicles then, Sir, for they don't read at all like our modern histories. They seem a much more religious sort of books.'

'Don't call them religious books,' said he, 'it puts one in mind of religious newspapers, – the greatest curse of our times. Yes, people sneer at the old English chroniclers now-a-days, and prefer the Edda, and all sorts of heathen stuff, to them; but they are great books, Sir, for those who have eyes for them; godly books is the name for them, written by God-fearing men, who were not ashamed of the faith which was in them; – men who believed, Sir, that a living God was ruling in England, and that in His name one of them might defy a thousand. Your historians, now-a-days, Sir, believe that Providence (for they dare not talk of God) is on the side of the strongest battalion. There's some difference, when you come to think of it, between the two creeds, Sir.'

The old gentleman looked at me quite fierce, so I made all the haste I could to change the subject.

'Don't you think it very curious, Sir, that the figure should have lasted all this time?' said I; 'because you see, Sir, if you or I were to cut a trench, two feet or so deep, up here, on the side of the hill, and stamp down the chalk ever so hard, it would be all filled up and grown over in a few years.'

'You are not the first person who has made that remark,' said he. 'In the year 1738, an antiquary of the name of Francis Wise, who lived at Oxford, visited the hill, and wrote a letter on the subject to Dr Mead, the most learned antiquary of that day. First he speaks of the figure of the horse as "being described in so masterly a manner that it may defy the painter's skill to give a more exact description of the animal."'

'How could he talk like that, Sir?' said I; 'why the figure isn't a bit like —'

'You are as bad as Camden,' said he, 'who talks of "I know not what shape of a horse fancied on the side of a whitish hill;" but the truth is, it is a copy of a Saxon standard, which, of course, was a rude affair. However, Wise, whom I was telling you of, goes on: —

'"When I saw it, the head had suffered a little and wanted reparation: and the extremities of his hinder legs, from their unavoidable situation, have by the fall of rains been filled up in some measure with the washings from the upper parts; so that, in the nearest view of him, the tail, which does not suffer the same inconvenience, and has continued entire from the beginning, seems longer than his legs. The supplies which nature is continually affording, occasion the turf to crumble and fall off into the white trench, which in many years' time produces small specks of turf, and not a little obscures the brightness of the Horse; though there is no danger from hence of the whole figure being obliterated, for the inhabitants have a custom of 'scouring the Horse,' as they call it; at which time a solemn festival is celebrated, and manlike games with prizes exhibited, which no doubt had their original in Saxon times in memory of the victory."'[17]

'Scouring the Horse! yes, of course,' said I, 'that is what they are doing now, and the games are to come off tomorrow.'

'Exactly so,' said he, 'but you will like to hear how Wise goes on: —

'"If ever the genius of King Alfred exerted itself (and it never failed him in his greatest exigencies), it did remarkably so upon account of this trophy. The situation of his affairs would not permit him to expend much time, nor his circumstances much cost, in effecting one" (truly, for he had six more pitched battles to fight between April and November). "His troops, though victorious, were harassed and diminished by continual duty; nor did the country afford, to any man's thinking, materials proper for a work of this king. Though he had not therefore the opportunity of raising, like other conquerors, a stupendous monument of brass or marble, yet he has shown an admirable contrivance, in erecting one magnificent enough, though simple in its design — executed, too, with little labour and no expense — that may hereafter vie with the Pyramids in duration, and perhaps exist when those shall be no more."'

'But, dear me, Sir,' said I, 'how can the White Horse vie with the Pyramids in duration? Why, the Pyramids were built –'

'Never mind when they were built,' said he; 'don't you see the old antiquary is an enthusiast? I had hoped you were one also.'

'Indeed, Sir, I am very anxious to hear all you can tell me,' said I, 'and I won't interrupt again.'

'Well, as to the scouring, Wise says: –

'"The ceremony of scouring the Horse, from time immemorial, had been solemnized by a numerous concourse of people from all the villages round about. I am informed, though the Horse stands in the parish of Uffington, yet other towns claim, by ancient custom, a share of the duty upon this occasion. Since, therefore, this noble antiquity is now explained, and consequently the reason of the festival, it were to be wished that, in order to prevent for the future its falling into oblivion, some care was taken of the regulation of the games, and that they were restored to their ancient splendour, of which, without question, they are fallen much short. I know that these rites are cavilled at and maligned by the more supercilious part of mankind; but the dislike to them seems to be founded merely upon the abuse of them to riot and debauchery, which I intend by no means to justify or excuse. The practice of the best and wisest states, whose maxims we approve and profess to follow, is sufficient authority for their use. The liberty we so justly boast, and which ought to be a common blessing to all, pleads loudly for them. The common people, from their daily labour, stands at least in as much need of proper intervals of recreation as their superiors, who are exempt from it, and therefore in all free states have been indulged in sports most suited to their genius and capacity. And if manlike games contribute anything towards the support of the natural bravery of these, who are to be our bulwark and defence in times of danger, they cannot be more seasonably revived than at this juncture, when, through the general luxury and dissoluteness of the age, there was never more likelihood of its being extinguished. Besides all this, from hence superior influence diffuseth itself through the better sort, who are supposed to enter further into the intention of these solemnities; for which reason it is, that to perpetuate to posterity the remembrance of great men, and of great actions, has been always recommended, as a proper incentive to virtue. Customs of very trifling import, some ridiculous in themselves, others owing to causes equally ridiculous, are oftentimes kept up by Englishmen with much zeal and tenacity; and shall the greatest prince that this isle was ever blessed with, and the greatest action of that prince's life, be in danger of being forgot, through the neglect of a solemnity, the only one perhaps, that was ever instituted, at least, that is now preserved, to his honour?"[18]

I didn't say a word now, though he seemed to have finished.

'Well,' said he, after a minute, 'have you nothing to say? You're very glad that it's over, I suppose?'

'No, Sir, indeed I am not,' said I; 'but I am very much obliged to you for your kindness in telling me all that you have.'

'You are a very intelligent young man, Sir,' said he; 'most young fellows of your age would have been bored to death half-an-hour ago, even if they hadn't managed to run off altogether, and so they would have lost a good lesson in English history – not that they would have cared much for that though. But now, I dare say you are getting hungry. Let us go up and see what they are doing in the Castle, and I shall be very glad if you will do me the honour of lunching with me.'

'Well,' thought I, as we got up from the turf, 'there are not many better things for getting a man on than being a good listener. Here is a very learned old gentleman who doesn't know my name, and I have got the length of his foot, and he has asked me to luncheon, just because I have been listening to his old stories. I wonder where the lunch is to be though? he spoke of a Castle, perhaps he lives in it – who knows?'

So we strolled away together up over the brow of the hill.

NOTES

1. See Simeon, AD 870
2. See Chronicle of St Neot, AD 878
3. See Saxon Chron. and Asser, AD 866
4. See Asser, AD 867
5. See Saxon Chron. and Huntingdon, AD 874
6. See Simeon, AD 870
7. NB. This was written in October, 1857
8. Here is Robert of Gloster's account of the martyrdom: –

So that atte laste to Estangle agen hym come:
Ther hii barned and robbede and that fole to grounde slowe;
And as wolves among ssep reulych hem to drowe,

Seynt Edmond was tho her kyng, and tho he sey that delvol cas
That me morthred so that fole, and non amendement n'as,
He ches levere to deye hym-sulf, that such soreve to ysey –
He dude hym vorth among ys ton, n'olde he nothyng fle.
Hii nome hym and scoured hym, and suthe naked hym bounde
To a tre, and to hym ssote, and made hym mony a wounde,
That the arewe were on hym tho thycke, that no stede n'as byleved.
Atte laste hii martred hym, and smyte of ys heved.
   Robert of Gloster's Chronicle, p.263, apud Thomas Hearne. Ed. 1724.

9.   See Saxon Chronicle, and Huntingdon, AD 870
10. See Brompton, AD 870
11. See Sax. Chron. AD 870
12. See Huntingdon, AD 871
13. See Simeon, AD 871
14. See Saxon Chronicle, AD 871
15. See Asser, AD 871
16. This is Robert of Gloster's account of the Battle: –

The Kyng and Alfred ys brother nome men ynowe,
Mette hem, and a batayle smyte up Assesdowne –
Ther was mony moder chyld, that sone lay ther doune –
The batayle ylaste vorte-nygt, and ther were aslawe
Vyf dukes of Dene-march, ar hii wolde wyth drawe,
And mony thousende of other men, and tho' gonne hii to fle;
Ac hii adde alle ybe assend, gyf the nyght n'adde y bee.
   *Robert of Gloster, p.263, apud Thomas Hearne. Ed.*1724.

17. Wise's Letter to Dr Mead, 'concerning some Antiquities in Berkshire,' ed. 1, pp. 25, 26.
18. Wise's Letter, p. 31.

CHAPTER IV

'WELL, here's the Castle, you see,' said he, when we had walked a few hundred yards, and were come quite to the top of the hill.

'Where, Sir?' said I, starting about. I had half expected to see and old stone building with a moat, and round towers and battlements, and a great flag flying; and that the old gentleman would have walked across the drawbridge, and cried out, 'What ho!, warder!' and that we should have been waited upon at lunch by an old white-headed man in black velvet, with a silver chain, and keys round his waist. Somehow, the story of the battle, and all the talk about Pendragon and Arthur, coming upon the back of the farm-house, and the out of the way country life, which was so strange to me, had carried me into a sort of new world; and I shouldn't have been much surprised to see a dragon running about the hill, though I should have been horribly frightened.

'I can't make up my mind about this Castle,' he went on, without noticing me: 'on two sides it looks like a regular Roman castrum, and Roman remains are found scattered about; but then the other sides are clearly not Roman. The best antiquaries who have noticed it call it Danish. On the whole, I think it must have been seized and occupied in succession by the lords of the country for the time being; and each successive occupier has left his mark more or less plainly. But, at any rate, you see it is a magnificent work.'

'Yes, Sir,' said I, 'no doubt;' though I own I was a good deal disappointed. For what do you think the Castle is? Up at the very top of the hill, above the White Horse, there is a great flat space, about as big as Lincoln's Inn Fields, only not the same shape, because it is only square on two sides. All round this space there is a bank of earth, eight or ten feet high in some places, but lower at others. Then, outside, there is a great, broad, deep ditch; it must be twenty-five feet from the top of the inner bank to the bottom of the ditch; and outside that again, is another large bank of earth, from the foot of which the downs slope away on every side. But the banks and ditch are all grown over with turf, just like the rest of the downs, and there isn't even a single stone, much less a tower, to be seen. There are three entrances cut through the double banks, one on the west, one on the south-east, and the third at the north-east side, which was the one through which we entered.

But if there were no warders and seneschals and drawbridges, there was plenty of life in the Castle. The whole place seemed full of men and women, and booths and beasts, and carts and long poles; and amongst them all were the Squire and Joe, and two or three farmers, who I afterwards found out were Committee-men, trying to get things into some sort of order. And a troublesome job they were having of it. All the ground was parcelled out for different purposes by the Committee, and such parts as were not wanted for the sports were let at small rents to any one who wanted them. But nobody seemed to be satisfied with his lot. Here a big gipsy, who wouldn't pay any rent at all, was settling his cart and family, and swinging his kettle, on a bit of ground, which the man who owned the pink-eyed lady had paid for. There a cheap-Jack was hustling a toyman from Wantage, and getting all his frontage towards the streets (as they called the broad spaces which were to be kept clear for the people to walk along). In another place, a licensed publican was taking the lot of a travelling showman into his skittle-alley. Then there were old women who had lost their donkeys and carts, and their tins of nuts and sacks of apples; and donkeys who had lost their old women, standing obstinately in the middle of the streets, and getting in everybody's way; and all round, saws and axes and hammers were going, and booths and stalls were rising up.

I shouldn't have liked to have had much to do with setting them all straight, and so I told Joe, when he came up to us, after we had been looking on at all the confusion for a minute or two. For most of the men were very rough-looking customers, like the costermongers about Covent Garden and Clare Market, and I know that those huckstering loafing blades are mostly terrible fellows to fight; and there wasn't a single policeman to look like keeping order. But Joe made light enough of it – he was always such a resolute boy, and that's what made me admire him so – and said, 'For the matter of that, if they were ten times as rough a lot and twice as many, the Squire and the farmers and their men would tackle them pretty quick, without any blue-coated chaps to help! Aye, and nobody knows it better than they, and you'll see they'll be all in nice order before sundown, without a blow struck; except amongst themselves, perhaps, and that's no matter, and what they're used to. But now, you come in,' said Joe, turning towards one of the large publicans' booths, which was already finished, 'the Committee have got a table here, and we must dine, for we shan't be home these four hours yet, I can see.'

'Sir,' said my new friend to Joe, drawing himself up a bit, but very politely; 'this gentleman is my guest. He has done me the honour of accepting my invitation to luncheon.'

'Oh! beg pardon, Sir, I'm sure,' said Joe; staring; 'I didn't know that Dick had any acquaintance down in these parts. Then,' said he to me, 'I shall take my snack with the rest presently; you'll see me about somewhere, when it's time to get back.' Joe went back into the crowd, and I followed the old gentleman.

We went into the booth, which was a very big one, made of strong double sail-cloth, stretched over three rows of fir poles, the middle row being, I should say, sixteen or eighteen feet high. Just on our right, as we entered from the street, was the bar, which was made with a double row of eighteen-gallon casks, full of ale, along the top of which boards were laid, so as to make a counter. Behind the bar the landlord and landlady, and a barmaid, were working away and getting everything into order. There were more rows of large casks, marked XX and XXX, ranged upon one another against the side of the booth, and small casks of spirits hooped with bright copper, and cigar boxes, and a table covered with great joints of beef and pork, and crockery and knives and forks, and baskets full of loaves of bread, and lettuces and potatoes. It must have cost a deal of money to get it all up the hill, and set the booth up. Beyond the bar was a sort of inner room, partly screened from the rest of the booth by a piece of sail-cloth, where a long table was laid out for luncheon, or 'nunching,' as the boots, who was doing waiter for the occasion, called it. The rest of the booth, except a space before the bar which was kept clear for casual customers to stand about in, was set about with rough tables and forms. We got a capital dinner; for the landlord knew my entertainer, and was very civil, and brought us our ale himself and poured it out, making an apology because it hadn't had quite time to fine down, but it would be a clear as a diamond, he said, if we would please call in tomorrow.

After we had done we went round behind the booth, where some rough planking had been put up to serve for stalls, and the boots, in his waiter's jacket, brought out the old gentleman's cob.

'Peter,' said he, when he had mounted, 'here is sixpence for you; and now mind what you are at, and don't get drunk and disgrace yourself up on the hill.'

Peter, who seemed to be very much afraid of the old gentleman, kept pulling away at his forelock, and hunching up his shoulders, till we turned the corner of the booth.

'Now I must be riding home,' said my friend, 'but if you like just walk round with me and I will show you the site of the battle.'

So I thanked him, and walked along by the side of his cob, and he rode out of the entrance we had come in by, and then round the outer earthwork of the castle. As we passed along, the inner bank rose high up on our right hand, and we could just see the tops of the highest booths above it.

'You see what a strong place it must have been before gunpowder was invented,' said the old gentleman; 'and here, you see, is the second entrance; and this road which we are upon is the Ridgeway, one of the oldest roads in England. How far it once extended, or who made it, no man knows; but you may trace it away there along the ridge of the downs as far as you can see, and in fact there are still some sixty miles of it left. But they won't be left long, I fear, Sir, in this age which venerates nothing.'

'I don't see much fear of that, Sir,' said I, 'after it has lasted so long already.'

'No fear, Sir!' said he, 'why miles of it have been ploughed up within my memory. God meant these downs, Sir, for sheep-walks, and so our fathers left them; but within the last twenty years would-be wise men have found that they will grow decent turnips and not very bad oats. Well, they plough them up, find two inches of soil only, get one crop out of them, and spoil them for sheep. Next year, no crops. Then comes manure, manure, manure; nothing but expense; not a turnip will trouble himself to grow bigger than a reddish under a pennyworth of guano or bones. The wise men grumble and swear, but the downs are spoiled.'

'But that will all cure itself then, Sir,' said I; 'they won't plough up any more, if it doesn't pay; and then the Ridgeway won't be touched!'

'They are all mad for ploughing, Sir, these blockhead farmers; why, half of them keep their sheep standing on boards all the year round. They would plough and grow mangold-wurzel on their fathers' graves. The Tenth Legion, Sir, has probably marched along this road; Severus and Agricola have ridden along it, Sir; Augustine's monks have carried the Cross along it. There is that in that old mound and ditch which the best turnips and oats in the world (if you could get them) can't replace. There are higher things in this world, Sir, than indifferent oats and d—d bad turnips.'

The old gentleman was all in a blaze again; he brought down his cane sharply on the cob's neck, which made him caper up and jump off along the Ridgeway, and it was a hundred yards before they drew up. I followed, thinking that he couldn't be a clergyman after all, to be swearing like that about nothing. When I got up to him, however, he was quite cool again He had stopped just below the western entrance to the Castle, and the ground fell rapidly in front of us.

'Now, you can't have a better point than this,' said he; 'you remember what I told you about armies. The Danes held the higher ground, that is, Uffington Castle, up here, behind us. Alfred, with his division of the Saxon army, lay over there, in that valley to the left, where you see the great wood in the middle of the down. That is Ashdown Park, Lord Craven's seat, and just on the edge of it there is a circular earthwork, which is called Alfred's camp. Aubrey says that in his time it was "almost quite defaced, by digging for the Sarsden stones to build my Lord Craven's house in the park;" but you may still find it if you look. Then, over there, on the point, a mile or more away to the right, is a camp called Hardwell Camp, where Æthelred lay. The crown of the slope you see along which the Ridgeway runs, is midway between the Saxon camps.

'In the early spring morning, the low call to arms passes round the height; the Danish host, marshalled behind the high earthworks, breaks over them, like an overflowing lake, and rushes down the slope. Alfred's division of the Saxon army is already on foot, and there he sits, the sickly stripling on the white horse, untried save in one luckless fight. How will he guide such a battle? See, his host is in motion; scouts fly out, riding for life across to Æthelred's camp. "Come up, my brother! the Pagan is upon us – while I live they shall not divide us – I will hold the crest of the Ridgeway, come life come death." The vans are together with a wild shout, squadron by squadron the hosts close up, the fight sways slowly backwards and forwards, the life's blood of a brave man pays for every inch won or lost. The Saxons are but one to three, the Pagans slowly overlap them – are on their flanks. The white horse and his rider dash from

side to side, faster and faster, as the over-matched Christians faint, reel, give back – now here, now there, along the line. When will the mass be over? Cut it short, as thou art Saxon man, oh priest! and get thee to sword and buckler.

'At last they come, Æthelred and his host – they are upon the right flank of the Pagan, and the fight is restored; and with many an ebb and pause, but steadily, through the long morning hours, rolls up the hill towards the camp and the fatal thorn.'

'Is that the old thorn-tree, then, do you think, Sir?' said I, pointing to one which was growing by itself some way off.

'I fear not, Sir, I fear not; the "unica spinosa arbor" is gone. It must have stood somewhere up here, on the slope just below the Castle, the stronghold of the Danish robbers. Here the grim Pagan turns to bay for the last time. King Bægseeg lies dead, a hundred yards below; by his side his standard-bearer and Earl Frœna; Halfdene is still unhurt, but near him Osbert totters under his shield; Harold can scarce back his charger, and the life-blood trickles slowly down his leg, and falls, drop by drop, on the trampled turf, as they still make front against Æthelred yonder – there on the right. But here, here the field must be won! This way, you Saxon men, kings-thane, and alderman! Whoever hath stout heart and whole body left.

'It is the old sea-king, Sidroc, "the ancient one of evil days;" mark him, as he bestrides his black war-horse, there by the old twisted thorn. His heavy sword drips with blood, his sword-arm is steeped in blood to the elbow – the dint of long and fierce battle is on horse and man; but the straight thin lips are set like flint in the midst of that grey beard, and the eyes glow and gleam under that fearful brow – eyes that have never quailed before conquering foe, or softened to the fallen – lips that have never opened to say the word "Spare." By his side the young Sidroc, grim son of grim sire. Ashdown crows must feast on those eyes, and Ashdown wolves pick those bones, if the Pagans are to be beaten this day. Again and again the advancing Saxons reel back from the stunted thorn, before the shock of the two Boersirkir. He comes! it is the sickly prince, the stripling on the white horse, trampling fetlock-deep in blood. Round him a chosen band of yellow-bearded men of Wessex. One moment's pause, and they meet in a last death-grapple. Bite, Saxon blade; pierce, Saxon spear! Think of your homes, my countrymen; think of the walls of Reading, of Ethelwulf and his last war-cry, "Our commander, Christ, is braver than they!" The black horse is down; young Sidroc springs over the brute, lashing out in death agony, and covers his father. His head is cleft to the chin – a half-armed gaunt cowherd drives his spear through the chest of the old sea-king. Away over their bodies up the hill go white horse, and stripling prince, and yellow-bearded men; rushing through the camp gate, scrambling over the banks pell-mell with the flying Pagan. The camp is ours; now slay while light is left – for there is no shelter for a Pagan between this and Reading. "Then were the horse-hoofs broken by the means of the prancings, of the prancings of their mighty ones. Oh my soul, thou hast trodden down strength!"'

The old gentleman stopped at last, and took off his hat and wiped his face, and then looked down at me as if he were half-ashamed –

'I see you think I'm mad –' he began.

'Indeed, sir –' said I, stammering a little.

'Well, well! never mind,' he said; 'the fact is, I live a good deal in those old times. I've been up here, and sat and gone over the fight so often, that when I get on the hillside, I think I saw it all. In the autumn evenings at twilight, when the south-wind blows wild, and the mist comes drifting over the broad downs, many a time, as I have stolen down the silent hillside, I have seen the weird old Pagan king and the five earls, sitting one on each of the giant's seats, and looking mournfully out over the vale, waiting – waiting – waiting for a thousand years, all but fourteen. It's a long time, sir, a long time; but you and I may have to wait for a longer over the scene of some of our doings. Who can say?'

I really now did begin to think the old gentleman a little crazy, so I said nothing. Presently he went on in his old quiet voice:–

'There, now I have dismounted my hobby, and am sane again. I live in a wild, lonely part of the world down west, and for the last thirty years have read little else but the Bible, and books 200 years old and upwards. Every man has his madness – that's mine – I don't get a chance of letting it out once a year. I have spent a very pleasant day with you, Sir; and if you ever come down to these parts again, and like to come on and see me, I shall be very glad. There is my name and address;' and he gave me his card, but he didn't say that I might publish it.

'Thank you, Sir,' said I, putting it into my pocket-book; 'but I hope you will be up on the hill tomorrow?'

'Yes, I shall just ride up,' he said, 'to see how they have used my old friend; he wanted scouring sadly. The games I don't much care about, though I'm glad they go on. But not one man in a thousand who will be on the hill tomorrow will know what the meaning of it all is; and that makes it a melancholy sight to me, Sir, on the whole.'

'But what a pity,' said I, 'that they are not told. It would interest everybody else, I'm sure, just as it has me. Why don't you tell it then, Sir, in a book or a newspaper?'

'Nobody would read my old-world stuff,' said he. 'No: a man must understand and be in sympathy with his own generation to coax it into caring about an older one. But now I must be going. If you have time to walk down to that little clump of trees over there, towards Æthelred's camp, you will find an old Druidical cromlech well worth examining. It is called Wayland Smith's cave. Walter Scott, who should have known better, says that the Danish king killed at Ashdown was buried there. He was no more buried there than in Westminster Abbey. Good-bye.' And so he put his cob into a canter, and went off along the Ridgeway.

When he was gone I walked down to the clump of trees and went into the cave; and then sat down on the great flat stone which covers it over, and finished putting down all I had heard from the old gentleman; and thought what odd people a man finds about the world, and how many things there are which one never heard of that other folk are spending their lives over. Then I went up to the camp again to find Joe, for the afternoon was getting on. True enough, as he had said, when I got back there I found it all getting into order. All along the north side were the theatres and peep-shows, and acrobats, and the pink-eyed lady, and the other shows. On the west side were the publicans' booths, some of them all ready, and others half-up, but all with their places settled; and the great street of huxters' stalls and cheap-Jacks was all set out along the south side, and as more and more of them came up they went off to the end of the line and pitched regularly. The gipsies and people with no regular business were all got away into a corner, behind the stalls. On the west side the county police were pitching their large tent close away by the bank, out of the way of everybody; and, some way in front of them, Lord Craven's people had put up two military-looking tents which I heard had belonged to the 42d Regiment, with a great flagstaff close by them. About the middle of the camp stood a large stage about six feet high, roped round for the backswording and wrestling. There was plenty of room now, and all the people who were not working at the booths and stalls were sitting about boiling kettles and getting their food. It was a very cheerful, pretty sight, up there out of the way of everything.

I soon found Joe, amongst a group of farmers and one or two young gentlemen, some on horseback and some on foot, standing round the Squire. They were talking over the arrangements before going home; and I stood a little way off, so as not to interrupt them or to seem to be pushing myself into their company.

'Now I think we have done all we can today,' said the Squire, gathering up his reins; 'but some of us must be up early tomorrow to get the lists made, and settle everything about the games.'

'About then o'clock, Sir?'

'Yes, that will do capitally. Now I shall just go and see how they have done the Horse.'

So he rode out of the camp, and we all followed over the brow of thi hill till we came to a good point for seeing the figure, which looked as bright and clean as a new sixpence.

'I think he'll do very well,' said the Squire.

'Listen to the scourers,' said one of the young gentlemen.

They had finished their work, and were sitting in a group round a large can of beer which the Squire had sent down to them; and one of them was singing a rumbling sort of ditty, with a tol-de-rol chorus, in which the rest joined lazily.

One of these young gentlemen gave me what he said were the words they were singing, afterwards, when I came to know him (as you will hear in the next chapter); and it seems he had found out that I was collecting all I could about the Horse. But I don't quite know whether he wasn't cutting his jokes upon me, for he is 'amazin' found of fun,' as Joe said; and for my part, I could never quite tell, when I was with him, whether he was in jest or earnest. However, here are the words he gave me:–

BALLAD OF THE SCOURING OF THE WHITE HORSE

The owld White Hoarse wants zettin to rights,
   And the Squire hev promised good cheer,
Zo we'll gee un a scrape to kip un in zhape,
   And a'll last for many a year.

A was made a lang lang time ago
   Wi a good dale o' labour and pains,
By King Alferd the Great when he spwiled their consate
   And caddled,* thay wosbirds† the Danes.

The Blewin Stwun in days gone by
   Wur King Alfred's bugle harn,
And the tharnin tree you med plainly zee
   As is called King Alferd's tharn.

There'll be backsword play, and climmin the powl,
   And a race for a peg, and a cheese,
And us thenks as hisn's a dummell‡ zowl
   As dwont care for zich spwoorts as theze.

---

* 'Caddle' – to worry: from cad, strife. – The Berkshire scholiast suggests, that the modern 'cad,' having regard to the peculiarities of the class, must be the same word.

† 'Wosbird,' bird of woe, of evil omen.

‡ 'Dummell,' dull, stupid.

When we had done looking at the Horse, some went one way and some another, and Joe and I down the hill to the Swan Inn, where we got the trap and started away for Elm Close.

'Why, Dick, how did you manage to pick up the old gentleman who was treating you at dinner?' said Joe; 'I suppose he's one of your London folk.'

''Twas he who picked me up,' said I, 'for I never set eyes on him before. But I can tell you he is a very learned party, and very kind too. He told me all about the battle of Ashdown, and ever so many more old stories. I should think he must have been two hours and more telling them.'

'Sooner you than I,' said Joe. 'Well, I thought I knew his face. He must be the old gent as was poking about our parish last fall, and sort of walking the bounds. Though there isn't any call for that, I'm sure, for we walk the bounds ourselves every year. The men as he hired told me he was looking after some old stone, the play stone I think he called it, and would have it he knew more about the names of the fields, and why they were called so, than they as had lived there all their lives. However, he stood 'em something handsome for their trouble. I expect he isn't quite right up here,' said he, touching his forehead and looking at me.

'Just as right as you,' said I, 'and I've no doubt he does know more about your parish than all of you put together. I think he must be some great antiquary.'

'Ah! that's what the Squire said when I told him. A great angular Saxon scholar he called him.'

'Anglo-Saxon, Joe,' said I, 'not angular.'

'Well, Anglo or angular, it's no odds,' said Joe; 'I calls it angular – that's good English at any rate.'

'But, Joe,' said I, 'I've taken down all he said, and should like to read it to you. I'm sure it would interest you.'

'Well, after supper tonight, over a pipe, perhaps,' said Joe; 'I ain't much of a hand at your old-world talk, you see. Or, I'll tell you what, you shall read it to Lu; she takes to book-learning and all that better than I.'

'I shall be very glad indeed to read it to your sister,' said I; 'and I daresay she can tell me something more.'

'May be,' said Joe, drawing his whip gently over the mare's loins; and then he began telling me about the talk he had had with the Squire.

He seemed to have been telling him all about his quarrel at the vestry with the other farmers, about keeping up the parish roads; and the Squire had smoothed him down, and given him some good advice as to how to get the roads made and the fences kept up without losing his temper. Joe owned to me that he was often falling out with some of his neighbours, or his hired men, when he couldn't get things quite his own way (for that's what it came to, and Joe is a warm-tempered fellow), and that he would sooner come six miles to get the Squire to 'tackle it,' than go to any other justice who lived nearer; 'for he knows our ways, and manages one way or another to get it out all straight without making a Sessions job of it,' said Joe, as we drove up to his gate; and though I was looking out to catch a sight of Miss Lucy, and hoping she might be out in the garden, I couldn't help allowing to myself that perhaps the country mightn't get on so much better after all if the unpaid magistracy were done away with.

Joe went off to the stable to see after his precious chestnut, and seemed to pity me because I didn't go with him. But I was off round the house and into the garden, to try and find Miss Lucy. When I did find her though, I wasn't quite pleased at first, as you may fancy when you hear what she was doing.

There is a trellis-work about eight feet high between the little flower garden and the kitchen garden, and in it a wicket-gate, through which runs a nice green walk by which you get from one to the other. The trellis-work is so covered with roses, and jessamine, and other creepers, that you can't see through, at least not in summer time; and I heard merry voices on the other side, but they couldn't hear me on the turf. So I hurried up to the wicket-gate; and the moment I got through, there I saw Miss Lucy, and close by her side a young man in a black coat, dark grey trousers, and a white tie. He had a great ribstone-pippin apple in one hand, off the best tree in the orchard, out of which he had taken a bite or two, which I thought was rather vulgar; and there he was, holding up his bitten apple and some of the creepers against the trellis-work, with both hands above Miss Lucy's head. And she stood there in her pretty white-straw hat, with the ribbons dangling loose over her shoulders, tying up the creepers to the trellis-work close to his face. I could see, too, that she was very well dressed, for she had on a pretty embroidered collar, as white as snow, with a nice bow of fresh pink ribbon in front; and the sleeves of her gown were loose, and fell back a little as she reached up with the string to tie the creepers, and showed her nice, white, round arms, which looked very pretty, only I wished she had waited for me to hold up the creepers instead of him. At her feet lay a basket full of apples and pears, and lavender and mignonette; so they must have been going about together for some time, picking fruit and flowers.

I stopped at the gate, and felt half inclined to go back; but he said something to her, and then she turned round and called me, so I walked up feeling rather sheepish. By the time I got up to them they had finished tying up the creeper, and she introduced me to Mr Warton, of London. He held out his hand, and said he had often heard Joseph speak of me, and was very glad to meet an old friend of his friend Hurst. So we shook hands, and he began eating his apple again, and she picked up her basket, and we walked together towards the house; but they were so free and pleasant together, and laughed and joked so, that it made me feel rather low, and I couldn't talk easily, though I did manage to say something about the White Horse, and how well it looked, and what a wonderful place it was up on the hill, when they asked me about it.

I wasn't sorry when she went in to look after the tea, and he sat down to write a letter. So I went round to the farm-yard to look for Joe, that I might find out from him about this Mr Warton. I found Joe with his fogger,[1] as he called him, looking at some calves, and thinking of nothing but them and the pigs. However, I stuck to him and praised all the beasts just as if I knew all about them, and so at last got him out of the yard; and then I told him there was a Mr Warton come.

'No! is he?' said he; 'I'm so glad. I was afraid he couldn't come down as he didn't answer my last letter.'

'Who is he, Joe?' said I.

'Haven't I told you?' said he; 'why, he's a parson up somewhere in London, and a real right sort. He was curate here for five years before he went up to town.'

'He seems to know Miss Lucy very well,' said I.

'Bless you, yes!' said Joe; 'Lu was in school, and he prepared her for her confirmation. He's the best company in the world, and not a bit proud, like some parsons. When he was down here, he used to drop in of an evening two or three times a week, and take his tea, or a bit of supper, just like you might.'

'He's a good bit older than we, though,' said I.

'Well, four or five years, maybe,' said Joe, looking rather surprised at me; 'I should say at least about thirty last grass, but I never asked him; what does it matter?' and so we got to the front door, and I went upstairs to my room to wash my hands before tea. I made myself as smart as I could, but I own I didn't half like the way this Mr Warton went on. However, I thought Miss Lucy must see he was too old for her.

As I was dressing, I turned the matter over with myself, how I was to behave downstairs. First, I thought I would try to ride the high horse, and be silent and vexed, and make them all uncomfortable; but then, thought I, will Miss Lucy see why I do it? It may be all out of love for her, and jealousy of this Mr Warton; and they say no young woman dislikes to see men jealous about her. But suppose she shouldn't see it in that light? Mightn't she only think, perhaps, that I was a very changeable and disagreeable sort of fellow? That would never do. Besides, after all, thought I, I'm down here at Joe's house, and I owe it to him to be as pleasant as I can. How's he to know that I am in love with his sister already? And this Mr Warton, too; he's a clergyman, and seems a very good sort, as Joe said; and then he has known them all so well, for so long; why am I to give myself airs because he likes talking to Miss Lucy? So I settled it in my own mind to go down with a smiling face, and to do all I could to make all the rest happy; and I felt much better myself when I had made up my mind.

There never was such a tea and supper (for we had them both together that night, as it was late) in the world; and I don't think I could have stood out five minutes if I had gone down in the sulks, as I thought of doing at first. The old lady, and Joe, and Miss Lucy, were all in great spirits at getting Mr Warton down; and he was just like a boy home for his holidays. He joked and rattled away about everything; except when they talked about any of his old parishioners or scholars, and then he was as kind and tender as a woman, and remembered all their names, and how many children there were in every family, and the sort of mistakes the boys and girls used to make in school. And he drew Miss Lucy out about the school, and Joe about the markets and the labourers, and the old lady about the best way of pickling cabbages, and me about London and my work, and shorthand, which he managed to find out that I could write in no time. So we were all in the best humour in the world, and pleased with one another and with him; and spent half an hour in praising him after he had gone upstairs to finish some writing which he had to do.

Then I asked them about the pastime, and what we should see next day on the hill. Miss Lucy began directly about the stalls and the sights, and the racing and the music; and cold dinner on the hill-side, and seeing all her friends in their best dresses. Joe listened to her for a bit, and then struck in –

'That's all very well for you women,' said he; 'but look here, Dick. If what I hear comes true, we shall have a fine treat on the stage; for they tell me there's a lot of the best old gamesters in Somersetshire coming up, to put in for the backsword prizes.'

'Then I'm sure I hope they won't be allowed to play,' said Miss Lucy.

'Not let to play!' said Joe; 'who put that into your head? Why, there's the printed list of the sports, and £12 prize for backswording, and £10 for wrestling.'

'Well, it's a great shame, then,' said Miss Lucy; 'for all the respectable people for miles round will be on the hill, and I think the gentlemen ought to stop them.'

'If they do, they'll spoil the pastime; for there won't be one man in twenty up there who'll care to see anything else. Eh, old fellow?' said Joe, turning to me at once.

'I agree with Miss Lucy,' said I; 'for I'm sure if the women are against these games, they can't be good for the men, and ought to be put down.'

'Dick, you're a cockney, and know no better,' said Joe, giving me a great spank on the back, which hurt a good deal and was very disagreeable, only I didn't say anything because I knew he meant it kindly; 'but as for you, Lucy, you, a west-country yeoman's daughter, to talk like that! If you don't take care, you sha'n't go up the hill to the pastime tomorrow at all; I'll leave you at home with mother,' and he shook his great fist at her.

'Won't I go up though?' said she, laughing; 'we'll see, Master Joe; why, I can walk up by myself, if it comes to that; besides, any of the neighbours will give me a lift – or here's Mr Richard, or Mr Warton. I'm sure –'

'What's that you're saying, Miss Lucy? What am I to do, eh?' and the parson walked in just as I was going to speak. I was vexed at his just coming in, and taking the word out of my mouth.

'Why I was telling Joe that you'll stop and take me up the hill, if he leaves me behind; won't you now, Mr Warton?'

'Leave you behind, indeed! here's a pretty to do!' said he, laughing. 'What in the world are you all talking about?'

'About the wrestling and backsword play,' struck in Joe; 'now she says –'

'Well now, I'll leave it to Mr Warton,' said Miss Lucy, interrupting him; 'I know he won't say it's right for men to be fighting upon a high stage before all the countryside.'

'Stuff and nonsense with your fighting!' said Joe; 'you know, sir, very well that they are old English games, and we sets great store by them down here, though some of our folk as ought to know better does set their faces against them now-a-days.'

'Yes, you know, Joe, that three or four clergymen have been preaching against them only last Sunday,' said Miss Lucy.

'Then they ain't the right sort, or they'd know better what to preach against. I don't take all for Gospel that the parsons say, mind you,' said Joe.

Miss Lucy looked shocked, but Mr Warton only laughed.

'Hullo, Joseph,' said he, 'speaking evil of your spiritual pastors! However, I won't say you're altogether wrong. Parsons are but men.'

'But, sir,' said I, quite confidently, 'I'm sure no clergyman can stand up for fighting and quarrelling.'

'Of course not,' said he; 'but what then?'

'Well, sir, these sports, as they call them, are just fighting and nothing else, and lead to all sorts of quarrels and bad blood, and so –'

'They don't lead to nothing of the kind,' shouted Joe; 'and you know nothing about it, Dick.'

'Now, Joe, at our last feast,' said Miss Lucy, 'didn't Reuben Yates get his head broken, and his arms all black and blue at backsword play?'

'Yes, and didn't you and mother patch him up with yards of diachylum, and give him his supper every night for a week, to come and be doctored and lectured? Rube liked his suppers well enough, and didn't mind the plastering and lecturing much; but if he don't go in tomorrow for the young gamesters' prize, my name ain't Joe Hurst.'

'Then he'll be a very ungrateful, wicked fellow,' said Miss Lucy.

'And you and mother won't give him any more suppers or diachylum,' said Joe; 'but I dare say he won't break his heart if you don't give him the preaching by itself. It does seem to me plaguy hard that the women won't let a man get his own head broke quietly, when he has a mind to it.'

'And there was Simon Withers, too,' went on Miss Lucy, 'he sprained his ankle at the wrestling, and was in the house for three weeks, and his poor old mother nearly starving.'

''Twasn't at wrestling though,' said Joe, ''twas at hurdle-racing. He'd much better have been at backswording; for a chap can go to work with a broken head next morning and feel all the better for it, but he can't with a sprained ankle.'

'What does Mr Warton think?' said I; for somehow he was keeping back, and seemed a little on Joe's side, and if he showed that, I thought he would lose ground with Miss Lucy.

'Oh! I'm sure Mr Warton is on our side, ain't you, Sir? Do tell Joe how wrong it is of him to go on talking as he does.'

'No, no, Miss Lucy, I'm not going to be drawn into the quarrel as your knight; you're quite able to take your own part,' said Mr Warton.

'I'm sure Mr Warton is against us in his heart,' said I to Miss Lucy; 'only he's a clergyman, and doesn't like to say so.'

'Come now, I can't stand that,' said he to me, 'and you and I must have it out; only mind, Miss Lucy, you mustn't come in; one at a time is enough for me.'

'I won't say a word, Sir, if Joe won't.'

'Very well,' said he, 'and now let's get our ground clear. Do you approve of the other sports, running matches, jumping matches, and all the rest?'

'Yes, Sir, of course I do,' said I.

'And you see no harm in one man beating another in a race for a prize?'

'No, Sir, no harm at all.'

'Well, but I suppose one must have activity and endurance to win in any of them?'

'Yes,' said I, 'and good pluck too, Sir. It takes as much heart I'm sure, any day, to win a hard race as a bout at backsword.'

'Very good,' said he. 'Then putting everything else aside, tell me which you think the best man, he who doesn't mind having his head broken, or he who does?'

'Well, Sir,' said I, beginning to fence a bit, for I thought I saw what he driving at, 'that depends on circumstances.'

'No, no,' said he, 'I want a short answer. We've nothing to do with circumstances. Suppose there were no circumstances in the world, and only two men with heads to be broken?'

'Well then, Sir,' said I, 'I suppose the one who doesn't mind having his head broken must be the best man.'

'Hah, hah!' laughed Joe, 'that puts me in mind of old Ben Thomson last feast. When he threw up his hat on the stage he said he could get his pint of beer any day for tuppence, but it wasn't every day as he could get his pint of beer and a broken head too for the same money.'

'Oh, but Mr Warton –' broke in Miss Lucy.

'Now you were not to say a word, you know,' said he.

'But Joe began, Sir.'

'Joseph, hold your tongue.'

'Very well, Sir,' said Joe, grinning.

'Then we come to this,' said he to me, 'a man must have just the same qualities to win at backsword as to win a race; and something else besides, which is good in itself?'

'But, Sir,' said I, 'that doesn't meet the point. What I say is, that backsword is a game in which men are sure to lose their tempers and become brutal.'

'But don't they sometimes lose their tempers in races?' said he.

'Yes, sometimes perhaps,' said I, 'but not often.'

'And sometimes they don't lose them at backsword?' said he.

'Well, perhaps not, Sir,'

'Then it seems that all that can be said against backsword is, that it is a harder trial of the temper than other games. Surely that's no reason for stopping it, but only for putting it under strict rules. The harder the trial the better. I'm sure that's good English sense.'

I didn't quite know what to say, but Miss Lucy broke in again.

'Oh, but Mr Warton, did you ever see any backsword play?'

'Now; Miss Lucy, that is against law,' said he; 'but I don't mind answering. I never did, and I dare say your champion never has.'

'No, Sir,' said I; 'but though you may have got the best of me, I don't believe you really mean that you think us wrong.'

'Would you, really, Sir, preach a sermon now in favour of backsword play and wrestling?' asked Miss Lucy, with a long face.

'What's that got to do with it, Lucy?' broke in Joe. 'We're not talking about preaching sermons, but about what's right for country chaps to do at pastimes.'

'Now, Joseph, I'm not going to ride off on any hobby of yours – besides, your sister's test is right. Several of your clergy about here have preached against these games, as was their duty if they had considered the subject well, and thought them wrong. I have never thought much about the matter till tonight. At present I think your clergy wrong. If I hold to that belief I would preach it; for I hope I never seriously say anything in the parlour which I wouldn't say in the pulpit.'

Just then, the tall clock in the passage outside gave a sort of cluck, which meant half-past nine o'clock, and Joe jumped up and opened the door for the servants, and gave Mr Warton the prayer-book. And then as soon as ever prayers were over, he bustled his mother and sister off to bed, though I could see that Miss Lucy wasn't half satisfied in her mind about the backsword play and wrestling, and wanted to stay and hear something more from Mr Warton. But Joe is always in a hurry for his pipe when half-past nine strikes, so we all had to humour him, and Mr Warton and I went with him into the kitchen to smoke our pipes.

NOTE

1   'Fogger' – quasi fodderer – he who giveth fodder to the cattle – generally used for the farmer's head man.

CHAPTER V

OW when we had fairly lighted up, and Joe had mixed us a glass of gin and water a piece, I felt that it was a very good time for me to have a talk about the White Horse and the scourings. I wasn't quite satisfied in my mind with all that the old gentleman had told me on the hill; and, as I felt sure that Mr Warton was a scholar, and would find out directly if there was anything wrong in what I had taken down, I took out my note-book, and reminded Joe that he had promised to listen to it over his pipe. Joe didn't half like it, and wanted to put the reading off, but Mr Warton was very good-natured about it, and said he should like to hear it – so it was agreed that I should go on, and so I began. Joe soon was dozing, and every now and then woke up with a jerk, and pretended he had been listening, and made some remark in broad Berkshire. He always talks much broader when he is excited, or half asleep, than when he is cool and has all his wits about him. But I kept on steadily till I had got through it all, and then Mr Warton said he had been very much interested, and believed that all I had taken down was quite correct.

'What put it into your head,' said he, 'to take so much interest in the Horse?'

'I don't know, Sir,' said I, 'but somehow I can't think of anything else now I have been up there and heard about the battle.' This wasn't quite true, for I thought more of Miss Lucy, but I couldn't tell him that.

'When I was curate down here,' said he, 'I was bitten with the same maggot. Nothing would serve me but to find out all I could about the Horse. Now, Joe, here, who's fast asleep –'

'No, he bean't,' said Joe starting, and giving a pull at his pipe, which had gone out.

'Well, then, Joe here, who is wide awake, and the rest, who were born within sight of him, and whose fathers fought at Ashdown, and have helped to scour him ever since, don't care half so much for him as we strangers do.'

'Oh! I dwon't allow that, mind you,' said Joe; 'I dwon't know as I cares about your long-tailed words and that; but for keeping the Horse in trim, and as should be, why, I be ready to pay –'

'Never mind how much, Joseph.'

Joe grinned, and put his pipe in his mouth again. I think he liked being interrupted by the Parson.

'As I was saying, I found out all I could about the Horse, though it was little enough, and I shall be very glad to tell you all I know.'

'Then, Sir,' said I, 'may I ask you any questions I have a mind to ask you about it?'

'Certainly,' said he; 'but you mustn't expect to get much out of me.'

'Thank you, Sir,' said I. 'A thousand years seems a long time, Sir, doesn't it? Now, how do we know that the Horse has been there all that time?'

'At any rate,' said he, 'we know that the Hill has been called, "White Horse Hill," and the Vale, the "Vale of White Horse," ever since the time of Henry the First; for there are cartularies of the Abbey of Abingdon in the British Museum which prove it. So, I think, we may assume that they were called after the figure, and that the figure was there before that time.'

'I'm very glad to hear that, Sir,' said I. 'And then about the scourings and the pastime? They must have been going on ever since the Horse was cut out?'

'Yes, I think so,' said he. 'You have got quotations there from Wise's letter, written in 1736. He says that the scouring was an old custom in his time. Well, take his authority for the fact up to that time, and I think I can put you in the way of finding out something, though not much, about most of the Scourings which have been held since.'

And he was as good as his word; for he took me about after the pastime to some old men in the neighbouring parishes, from whom I found out a good deal that I have put down in this chapter. And the Squire, too, when Joe told him what I was about, helped me.

Now I can't say that I have found out all the Scourings which have been held since 1736, but I did my best to make a correct list, and this seems to be the proper place to set it all down.

Well, the first Scouring, which I could find out anything about, was held in 1755, and all the sports then seem to have been pretty much the same as those of the present day. But there was one thing which happened which could not very well have happened now. A fine dashing fellow, dressed like a gentleman, got on to the stage, held his own against all the old gamesters, and in the end won the chief prize for the backsword-play, or cudgel-play, as they used to call it.

While the play was going on there was plenty of talk as to who this man could be, and some people thought they knew his face. As soon as he had got the prize he jumped on his horse, and rode off. Presently, first one, and then another, said it was Tim Gibbons, of Lambourn, who had not been seen for some years, though strange stories had been afloat about him.

It was the Squire who told me the story about Tim Gibbons; but he took me to see an old man who was a descendant of Tim's, and so I think I had better give his own account of his ancestor and his doings. We found the old gentleman, a hale, sturdy old fellow, working away in a field at Woolstone, and, as near as I could get it, this was what he had to say about the Scouring of 1755:–

Squire. 'Good morning, Thomas. How about the weather? Did the White Horse smoke his pipe this morning?'

Thos. 'Mornin', Sir. I didn't zee as 'a did. I allus notices he doos it when the wind blaws moor to th' east'ard. I d'wont bode no rain today, Sir.'

Squire. 'How old are you, Thomas?'

Thos. 'Seventy year old this Christmas, Sir. I wur barn at Woolstone, in the hard winter, when I've heard tell as volks had to bwile their kettles wi' the snaw.'

Squire. 'I want to know something about your family, Thomas.'

Thos. 'Well, Sir, I bean't no ways ashamed of my family, I can assure'ee. I've a got two zons, and vour daaters. One on 'em, that's my oldest bwoy, Sir, wur all droo' the Crimee wars, and never got a scratch. In the Granadier guards, Sir, he be. A uncommon sprack[1] chap, Sir, though I says it, and as bowld as a lion; only while he wur about our village wi' t'other young chaps, he must allus be a fighting. But not a bad-tempered chap, Sir, I assure'ee. Then, Sir –'

Squire. 'But, Thomas, I want to know about those that came before you. What relation was Timothy Gibbons, whom I've heard folks talk about, to you?'

Thos. 'I suppose as you means my great-grandvather, Sir.'

Squire. 'Perhaps so, Thomas. Where did he live, and what trade did he follow?'

Thos. 'I'll tell 'ee, Sir, all as I knows; but somehow, vather and mother didn't seem to like to talk to we bwoys about 'un.'

Squire. 'Thank 'ee, Thomas. Mind, if he went wrong it's all the more credit to you, who have gone straight; for there isn't a more honest man in the next five parishes.'

Thos. 'I knows your meanings good, and thank 'ee kindly, Sir, tho' I be no schollard. Well, Timothy Gibbons, my great grandvather, you see, Sir, foller'd blacksmithing at Lambourn, till he took to highway robbin', but I can't give 'ee no account o' when or wher'. Arter he'd been out, may be dree or vour year, he and two companions cum to Baydon; and whilst hiding theirselves and baiting their hosses in a barn, the constables got ropes round the barnyard and lined 'em in. Then all dree drawed cuts[2] who was to go out fust and face the constables. It fell to Tim's two companions to go fust, but their hearts failed 'em, and they wouldn't go. So Tim cried out as "he'd shew 'em what a Englishman could do," and mounted his hos and drawed his cutlash, and cut their lines a-two, and galloped off clean away; but I understood as t'other two was took. Arter that, may be a year or two, he cum down to a pastime on White Hos Hill, and won the prize at backswording; and when he took his money, fearing lest he should be knowed, he jumped on his hos under the stage, and galloped right off, and I don't know as he ever cum again to these parts. Then I've understood as things throve wi' 'un, as 'um will at times, Sir, wi' thay sort o' chaps, and he and his companions built the Inn called "the Magpies," on Hounslow Heath; but I dwon't know as ever he kep' the house hisself, except it med ha' been for a short while. Howsomever, at last he was took drinking at a public-house, someweres up Hounslow way, wi' a companion who played a cross wi' 'un, and I b'live 'a was hanged at Newgate. But I never understood as he killed anybody, Sir, and a'd used to gie some o' the money as he took to the poor, if he knowed they was in want.'

Squire. 'Thank 'ee, Thomas. What a pity he didn't go soldiering; he might have made a fine fellow then!'

Thos. 'Well, Sir, so t'wur, I thinks. Our fam'ly be given to that sort o' thing. I wur a good hand at elbow and collar wrastling myself, afore I got married; but then I gied up all that, and ha' stuck to work ever since.'

Squire. 'Well, Thomas, you've given me the story I wanted to hear, so it's fair I should give you a Sunday dinner.'

Thos. 'Lord love 'ee, Sir, I never meant nothin' o' that sort; our fam'ly –'

We were half-way across the field, when I looked round, and saw old Thomas still looking after us and holding the Squire's silver in his hand, evidently not comfortable in his mind at having failed in telling us all he had to say about *his fam'ly,* of which he seemed as proud as any duke can be of his, and I dare say has more reason for his pride than many of them. At last, however, as we got over the stile, he pocketed the affront and went on with his work.

I could find out nothing whatever about the next Scouring; but I was lucky enough to get the printed hand-bill which was published before the one in 1776, which I made out to be the next but one after that at which Tim Gibbons played.

When I showed this old hand-bill to the Parson he was very much tickled. He took up the one which the Committee put out this last time, and looked at them together for a minute, and then tossed them across to me.

'What a queer contrast,' said he, 'between those two bills.'

'How do you mean, Sir?' said I; 'why the games seem to be nearly the same.'

'So they are,' said he; 'but look at the prizes. Our great grandfathers you'll see gave no money prizes; we scarcely any others. The gold-laced hat and buckskin breeches have gone, and current coin of the realm reigns supreme. Then look at the happy-go-lucky way in which the old bill is put out. No date given, no name signed! who was responsible for the breches, or the shoe-buckles? And then, what grammar! The modern bill, you see, is in the shape of resolutions passed at a meeting, the chairman's name being appended as security for the prizes.'

'That seems much better and more business-like,' said I.

'Then you see the horse race for a silver cup has disappeared,' he went on. 'Epsom and Ascot have swallowed up the little country races, just as big manufacturers swallow up little ones, and big shops whole streets of little shops, and nothing but monsters flourish in this age of unlimited competition and general enlightenment. Not that I regret the small country town-races, though.'

'And I see, Sir, that "smocks to be run for by ladies" is left out in the modern bill.'

'A move in the right direction there, at any rate,' said he, 'the bills ought to be published side by side.' So I took his advice, and here they are:–

WHITE HORSE HILL, BERKS, 1776.*	PASTIME
The scowering and cleansing of the White Horse is fixed for Monday the 27th day of May; on which day a Silver Cup will be run for near White Horse Hill, by any horse, &c. that never run for anything, carrying 11 stone, the best of 3 two-mile heats, to start at ten o'clock.	*To be held on the occassion of the Scouring of the White Horse, September 17th and 18th, 1857.*
	At a meeting held at the Craven Arms, Uffington, on the 20th day of August, 1857, the following resolutions (amongst others) were passed unanimously:–
Between the heats will be run for by Poneys, a Saddle, Bridle and Whip; the best of 3 two-mile heats, the winner of 2 heats will be entitled to the Saddle, the second best the Bridle, and the third the Whip.	First. That a pastime be held on the White Horse Hill on Thursday and Friday, the 17th and 18th of September, in accordance with the old

The same time a Thill harness will be run for by Cart-horses, &c. in their harness and bells, the carters to ride in smock frocks without saddles, crossing and jostling, but no whipping allowed.

A flitch of Bacon to be run for by asses.

A good Hat to be run for by men in sacks, every man to bring his own sack.

A Waistcoat, 10s. 6d. value, to be given to the person who shall take a bullet out of a tub of flour with his mouth in the shortest time.

A Cheese to be run for down the White Horse Manger.

Smocks to be run for by ladies, the second best of each prize to be entitled to a Silk Hat.

Cudgel-playing for a *gold-laced Hat* and a pair of buckskin Breeches, and *Wrestling* for a pair of silver Buckles and a pair of pumps.

The horses to be on the White Horse Hill by nine o'clock.

No less than four horses, &c. or asses to start for any of the above prizes.

custom at the time of 'The Scouring of the Horse.'

2ndly. That E. Martin Atkins, Esq. of Kingston Lisle, be appointed Treasurer.

3rdly. That prizes be awarded for the following games and sports, That is to say –

Backsword Play { Old gamesters, £8. Young gamesters, £4.
Wrestling: { Old gamesters, £5. Young gamesters, £4.

A jingling match.

Foot races.

Hurdle races

Race of cart-horses in Thill harness (for a new set of harness).

Donkey race (for a flitch of bacon).

Climbing pole (for a leg of mutton).

Races down 'the Manger' (for cheese).

A pig will be turned out on the down, to be the prize of the man who catches him (under certain regulations); and further prizes will be awarded for other games and sports as the funds will allow.

4thly. That no persons be allowed to put up or use a stall or booth on the ground, without the previous sanction of Mr Spackman, of Bridgecombe Farm (the occupier), who is hereby authorized to make terms with any person wishing to put up a stall or booth.

Signed, E. MARTIN ATKINS,
Chairman.

* This hand-bill was kindly given to me by H. Godwin, Esq. of Newbury.

Then came a Scouring on Whit-Monday, May 15th, 1780, and of the doings on that occasion there is the following notice in the *Reading Mercury* of May 22nd, 1780:–

'The ceremony of scowering and cleansing that noble monument of Saxon antiquity, the White Horse, was celebrated on Whit-Monday, with great joyous festivity. Besides the customary diversions of horse-racing, foot-races, &c., many uncommon rural diversions and feats of activity were exhibited to a greater number of spectators than ever assembled on any former occasion. Upwards of thirty thousand persons were present, and amongst them most of the nobility and gentry of this and the neighbouring counties; and the whole was concluded without any material accident. The origin of this remarkable piece of antiquity is variously related; but most authors describe it as a monument to perpetuate some signal victory, gained near the spot, by some of our most ancient Saxon princes. The space occupied by this figure is more than an acre of ground.'

I also managed to get a list of the games, which is just the same as the one of 1776, except that in addition there was, 'a jingling match by eleven blindfolded men, and one unmasked and hung with bells, for a pair of buckskin breeches.'

The Parson found an old man, William Townsend by name, a carpenter at Woolstone, whose father, one Warman Townsend, had run down the manger after the fore-wheel of a wagon, and won the cheese at this Scouring. He told us the story as his father had told it to him, how that 'eleven on 'em started, and amongst 'em a sweep chimley and a millurd; and the millurd tripped up the sweep chimley and made the zoot flee a good 'un;' and how 'the wheel ran pretty nigh down to the springs that time,' which last statement the Parson seemed to think couldn't be true. But old Townsend knew nothing about the other sports.

Then the next Scouring was held in 1785, and the Parson found several old men who could remember it when they were very little. The one who was most comunicative was old William Ayres of Uffington, a very dry old gentleman, about eighty-four years old:–

'When I wur a bwoy about ten years old,' said he, 'I remembers I went up White Hoss Hill wi' my vather to a pastime. Vather'd brewed a barrel o' beer to sell on the Hill–a deal better times then than now, Sir!'

'Why, William?' said the Parson.

'Augh! bless'ee, Sir, a man medn't brew and sell his own beer now: and oftentimes he can't get nothin' fit to drink at thaay little beer-houses as is licensed, nor at some o' the public-houses too for that matter. But 'twur not only for that as the times wur better then, you see, Sir –'

'But about the sports, William?'

'Ees Sir, I wur gandering sure enough,' said the old man: 'well now, there wur Varmer Mifflin's mare run for and won a new cart-saddle and thill-tugs – the mare's name wur *Duke*. As many as a dozen or moor horses run, and they started from Idle's Bush, which wur a vine owld tharnin'-tree in thay days – a very nice bush. They started fromIdle's Bush, as I tell 'ee, Sir, and raced up to the Rudge-waay; and Varmer Mifflin's mare had it all the way, and beat all the t'other on 'um holler. The pastime then wur a good 'un – a wunderful sight o' volks of all sorts, rich and poor. John Morse of Uffington, a queerish sort of a man, grinned agin another chap droo' hos collars, but John got beaat – a fine bit of spwoort to be shure, Sir, and made the folks laaf. Another geaam wur to bowl a cheese down the Mainger, and the first as could catch 'un had 'un. The cheese was a tough 'un and held together.'

'Nonsense, William, that's impossible,' broke in the Parson.

'Augh Sir, but a did though, I assure 'ee,' persisted William Ayres, 'but thaay as tasted 'un said a warn't very capital arter all.'

'I daresay,' said the Parson, 'for he couldn't have been made of anything less tough than ash pole.'

'Hah, hah, hah,' chuckled the old man, and went on.

'There wur running for a peg too, and they as could ketch 'un and hang 'un up by the tayl had 'un. The girls, too, run races for smocks – a deal of pastime, to be sure, Sir. There wur climmin' a grasy pole for a leg of mutton, too; and backsoordin', and wrastlin', and all that, ye knows, Sir. A man by the name of Blackford, from the low countries, Zummersetshire, or that waay some weres, he won the prize, and wur counted the best hand for years arter, and no man couldn't break his yead; but at last, nigh about twenty years arter, I'll warn[3] 'twur – at Shrin'um Revel, Harry Stanley, the landlord of the Blawin' Stwun, broke his yead, and the low-country men seemed afeard o' Harry round about here for long arter that. Varmer Small-bwones of Sparsholt, a mazin' stout man, and one as scarce no wun go where 'a would could drow down, beaat all the low-country chaps at wrastlin', and none could stan' agean 'un. And so he got the neam o' Varmer Greaat Bwones. 'Twur only when he got a drap o' beer a leetle too zoon, as he wur ever drowed at wrastlin', but they never drowed 'un twice, and he had the best men come agean 'un for miles. This wur the first pastime as I well remembers, but there med

ha' been some afore, for all as I knows. I ha' got a good memoran-
dum, Sir, and minds things well when I wur a bwoy, that I does. I
ha' helped to dress the White Hoss myself, and a deal o' work 'tis to
do't as should be, I can asshure 'ee, Sir. About Claay Hill, 'twixt
Fairford and Ziziter, I've many a time looked back at 'un, and 'a
looks as nat'ral as a pictur, Sir.'

Between 1785 and 1803 there must have been at least two
Scourings, but somehow none of the old men could remember the
exact years, and they seemed to confuse them with those that came
later on, and though I looked for them in old county papers, I could
not find any notice of them.

At the Scouring of 1803, Beckingham of Baydon won the prize at
wrestling; Flowers and Ellis from Somersetshire won the prize at
backsword play; the waiter at the Bell Inn, Farringdon, won the
cheese race, and at jumping in sacks; and Thomas Street, of Niton,
won the prize for grinning through horse collars, 'but,' as my
informant told me, 'a man from Woodlands would ha' beaat, only
he'd got no teeth. This geaam made the congregation laaf 'mazinly.'

Then came a Scouring in 1808, at which the Hanney men came
down in a strong body and made sure of winning the prize for
wrestling. But all the other gamesters leagued against them, and at
last their champion, Belcher, was thrown by Fowler of Baydon; –
both these men are still living. Two men, 'with very shiny top-boots,
quite gentlemen, from London,' won the prize for backsword play,
one of which gentlemen was Shaw, the life-guardsman, a Wiltshire
man himself as I was told, who afterwards died at Waterloo after
killing so many cuirassiers. A new prize was given at this pastime
and a very blackguard one, viz., a gallon of gin or half a guinea for
the woman who would smoke most tobacco in an hour. Only two
gipsey women entered, and it seems to have been a very abominable
business, but it is the only instance of the sort that I could hear of at
any Scouring.

The old men disagree as to the date of the next Scouring, which
was either in 1812 or 1813; but I think in the latter year, because the
clerk of Kingstone Lisle, an old Peninsula man, says that he was at
home on leave in this year, and that there was to be a Scouring. And
all the people were talking about it when he had to go back to the
wars. At this Scouring there was a prize of a loaf made out of a
bushel of flour, for running up the manger, which was won by Philip

New, of Kingstone-in-the-Hole; who cut the great loaf into pieces at the top, and sold the pieces for a penny a piece. I am sure he must have deserved a great many pennies for running up that place, if he really ever did it; for I would just as soon undertake to run up the front of the houses in Holborn. The low country men won the first backsword prize, and one Ford, of Ashbury, the second; and the Baydon men, headed by Beckingham, Fowler, and Breakspear, won the prize for wrestling. One Henry Giles (of Hanney, I think they said) had wrestled for the prize, and I suppose took too much beer afterwards; at any rate, he fell into the canal on his way home, and was drowned. So the jury found, 'Killed at Wrastlin';' 'though,' as my informant said, ''twur a strange thing for a old geamster as knew all about the stage, to be gettin' into the water for a bout. Hows'mever, Sir, I hears as they found it as I tells 'ee, and you med see it any day as you've a mind to look in the parish register.'

Then I couldn't find that there had been another Scouring till 1825, but the one which took place in that year seems by all accounts to have been the largest gathering that there has ever been. The games were held at the Seven Barrows, which are distant two miles in a south-easterly direction from the White Horse, instead of in Uffington Castle; but I could not make out why. These seven barrows, I heard the Squire say, are probably the burial-places of the principal men who were killed at Ashdown, and near them are other long irregular mounds, all full of bones huddled together anyhow, which are very likely the graves of the rank and file.

After this there was no Scouring till 1838, when on the 19th and 20th of September, the old custom was revived, under the patronage of Lord Craven. The *Reading Mercury* congratulates its readers on the fact, and adds that no more auspicious year could have been chosen for the revival, 'than that in which our youthful and beloved Queen first wore the British crown, and in which an heir was born to the ancient and noble house of Craven, whom God preserve.' I asked the Parson if he knew why it was that such a long time had been let to pass between the 1825 Scouring and the next one.

'You see it was a transition time,' said he; 'old things were passing away. What with Catholic Emancipation, and Reform, and the new Poor Law, even the quiet folk in the Vale had no time or heart to think about pastimes: and machine-breaking and rick-burning took the place of wrestling and backsword play.'

'But then, Sir,' said I, 'this last fourteen years we haven't had any Reform Bill (worse luck) and yet there was no Scouring between 1843 and 1857.'

'Why can't you be satisfied with my reason?' said he; 'now you must find one out for yourself.'

The last Scouring, in September, 1843, Joe had been at himself, and told me a long story about, which I should be very glad to repeat, only I think it would rather interfere with my own story of what I saw myself. The Berkshire and Wiltshire men, under Joe Giles of Shrivenham, got the better of the Somersetshire men, led by Simon Stone, at backsword play; and there were two men who came down from London, who won the wrestling prize away from the countrymen. 'What I remember best, however,' said Joe, 'was all the to-do to get the elephant's caravan up the hill, for Wombwell's menagerie came down on purpose for the Scouring. I should think they put-to a matter of four-and-twenty horses, and then stuck fast four or five times. I was a little chap then, but I sat and laughed at 'em a good one; and I don't know that I've seen so foolish a job since.'

'I don't see why, Joe,' said I.

'You don't?' said he, 'well, that's good, too. Why didn't they turn the elephant out and make him pull his own caravan up? He would have been glad to do it, poor old chap, to get a breath of fresh air, and a look across the vale.'

But now that I have finished all that I have to tell about the old Scourings (at least all that I expect anybody will read), I must go back again to the kitchen on the night of the 16th of September, 1857. Joe, who, as I said, was half asleep while I was reading, soon waked up afterwards, though it was past eleven o'clock, and began to settle how we were to go up to the hill the next morning.

'Now I shall ride the chestnut up early,' said he, ''cause I may be wanted to help the Squire and the rest, but it don't matter for the rest of you. I'll have a saddle put on my old brown horse, and he'll be quiet enough, for he has been at harvest work, and the four-wheel must come up with Lu somehow. Will you ride or drive, Sir?' said he, turning to the Parson.

'Oh, I don't mind; whichever is most convenient,' said Mr Warton.

'Did'st ever drive in thy life, Dick?' said Joe to me.

I was very near saying 'yes,' for I felt ashamed of not being able to do what they could; however, I told the truth, and said 'no;' and next minute I was very glad I had, for, besides the shame of telling a lie, how much worse it would have been to be found out by Miss Lucy in the morning, or to have had an upset or some accident.

So it was settled that Mr Warton should drive the four-wheel, and that I should ride the old horse. I didn't think it necessary to say that I had never ridden anything but the donkeys on Hampstead Heath, and the elephant in the Zoological Gardens. And so, when all was settled, we went to bed.

NOTES

1 'Sprack,' – sprightly.
2 'Draw cuts,' – to draw lots.
3 'Warn,' – contraction of the word 'warrant'.

CHAPTER VI

NEXT morning I got up early, for I wasn't quite easy in my mind about riding Joe's old horse, and so I thought I would just go round and look at him, and ask the fogger something about his way. It was a splendid morning, not a cloud to to be seen. I found the fogger strapping away at the horses. Everybody had been up and about since daylight, to get their day's work done, so that they might get away early to the pastime. All the cows had been milked and turned out again, and Joe was away in the fields, looking after his men.

I stood beating about the bush for some time, for I didn't want to let the man see what I was thinking of if I could help it. However, when he brought out the old brown horse to clean him down, I went up and patted him, and asked whether he was a good saddle horse.

'Ees, there warn't much fault to find wi' un,' said the fogger, stopping his hissing and rubbing for a moment, 'leastways for them as didn't mind a high goer.'

I didn't quite know what he meant by a high goer, so I asked him if the brown was up to my weight.

'Lor' bless 'ee, ees. He'd make no account o' vivteen stun. Be you to ride un up the hill, Sir, make so bold?' said he.

'Yes, at least I think so,' said I.

'Hev 'ee got arra loose tooth, Sir?' said he, grinning.

'No,' said I, 'why?'

''Cause he'll be as likely as not to shake un out for 'ee, Sir, if you lets un hev his head up on the downs.'

I didn't like this account of the brown horse, for as I hadn't ridden much, he might take his head perhaps whether I let him have it or not. So I made up my mind not to ride. I thought I would go behind in the four-wheel, for I didn't like to leave Miss Lucy all alone with the Parson for so long; but then I found that one of the carter-boys was to go behind to look after the horses, and I didn't choose to be put up side by side with him, to look ridiculous. There was a big wagon going up, too, full of the farm servants, but that didn't seem to suit me any better, so I settled with myself that I would just start and walk up.

Joe, luckily for me, thought he had settled everything, and so at breakfast said nothing more about the old horse; though I was afraid he would every minute, and then I should have had to pretend I was going to ride, or they might have found out that I didn't quite like the notion. I was very glad when I saw him fairly off after breakfast, cantering away on the chestnut: and, very soon afterwards, I took a good stout stick of Joe's in my hand, put my note-book in my pocket, and started off quietly by myself.

At first as I walked along I didn't enjoy myself much for thinking of the four-wheel, and I was almost getting jealous of the Parson again. But I soon got over it, when I remembered how kind he had been the night before. And I felt, too, that if he really was making up to her there was very little chance for me, so I had better make up my mind anyhow to see and enjoy everything I could. I don't think I was very much in love at the time: if it had been a week later I should have found it much harder perhaps.

I kept along the shady side of the road, for it was getting hot already, and crossed the canal, and kept making up towards the hills. I wasn't sure of the way, but I knew that if once I got up the hill I should find the Ridgeway, and could follow it all the way up to the Castle. After a bit I fell in with groups of people, all going the same way; and so, following on with them, after about an hour's walk, I came to the foot of the hills; and found a pretty little inn, standing back from the road, nestled into a plantation, where everybody else seemed to be stopping; and so I stopped too, and sat down on the bench before the door to have a glass of beer before facing the pull up to the top.

In front of the door was an oak tree, and under the tree a big stone with some curious holes in it, into which pieces of wood were fitted, secured by a padlock and chain. I was wondering what it could be, when the landlord came out with some of his guests, and pulling out a key unlocked the padlock, and took the pieces of wood out of the holes. Then there was some talk between the young men and their sweethearts, and first one and then another stooped down and blew into the hole at the top, and the stone made a dull moaning sound,

unlike anything I had ever heard. The landlord told me that when it was well blown on a still day, it could be heard for four or five miles, and I should think it could; for I left them blowing away when I started again, and heard the sound every now and then until I was close up to the Castle, though the wind blew from the south, and down the hill.

I should think a dozen parties, in all sorts of odd go-carts and other vehicles, or on foot, must have passed the Blowing-stone in the ten minutes which I spent on the bench. So I got quite eager to be up at the Castle, and paid for my beer and started again. It is a very long stiff pull up Blowing-stone Hill, and the road is not a very good one; so I soon began to pass the gigs and carts, most of which had to stop every hundred yards or so, to let the horses and donkeys get their wind. Half way up, in the worst part of the hill, I found an old huckstering woman and a boy in great trouble. They had a little cart laden with poles and boards for a stall, and two great sacks of nuts and sweetstuff: and only one donkey in the shafts, who had got one wheel of the cart into a deep chalk rut, and stood there like a post. The woman and boy were quite beat with dragging at his head, and trying to lift the wheel out of the rut, and as I came up she was 'fairly giving out.'

'Lawk-a-massy! how ever be I to scawt[1] up? Do'ee lend a help, there's a good soul,' said she to me.

Well, I couldn't go by and leave her there, though I didn't half like having to stop: so I helped to lift the wheel out, and then we pushed the cart up a few yards, and the old donkey tried to sidle it into another rut, and we had another fight with him. My blood got up at his obstinacy; I don't believe there ever was another such a donkey in the world; so the more he backed and sidled, the more I and the old woman and the boy fought. And then the people that passed us began to laugh and joke at us, and I got angry at them, and the old woman, and everybody; but I set my teeth, and made up my mind to get him up to the top if I stayed there all day.

I should think we must have been nearly half-an-hour at work, and had got on about three hundred yards or so, when a fine dog-cart on high wheels came up. I heard the gentlemen in it talking and laughing as they came near us; but I didn't look up, and kept working away at the donkey, for I was afraid they would only joke at us.

'Oh deary me, deary me, Master Gaarge, be that you?' I heard the old woman call out; 'now do'ee stop some o' the chaps, and tell 'em to help. I be nigh caddled to death wi' this drattled old jack-ass – oh dear, oh dear!'

'Why, Betty! what in the world are you after?' said a merry voice, which I thought I had heard before; and looking up, I saw the young gentleman who had promised me the song.

'Oh, you see, master Gaarge, I though as I might turn a honest penny if I could only win up to the pastime wi' some nuts and brandy-balls. So I loaned neighbour Tharne's cart as he fetches coals from the canal wi', and his ass – and if 'twas Balaam's ass hisself he couldn't be no wus – and here I be; and if it hadn't a been for this kind gentleman' –

'Well, stop your talk, Betty, and take hold of his head,' said he, jumping out of his dog-cart and giving the reins to the one who was beside him. 'Ah, good morning,' nodding to me, as he came to the back of the cart, 'now then, with a will! shove away!'

So we shoved the cart against the donkey's legs. 'Don't pull, Betty, let him have his head; just keep hold of reins. Look out, boy; stop him making for the ditch;' and away went Master Neddy scrambling up hill, for he found that the cart was coming over his back if he didn't move on. Master George was as strong as a ballast heaver, and the donkey seemed to find it out quick enough, for we were up the hill in no time.

'Bless your kind heart, Master Gaarge!' almost sobbed the old woman; 'I be all straight now. Do'ee hev summat to suck now, or some nuts, and this kind gentleman too; you allus wur fond o' suck;' and she begun untying the neck of one of her sacks.

'Oh, Betty, you wicked old lone woman!' said he, 'haven't you made me ill often enough with your nastinesses fifteen years ago?'

'Dwont'ee, now, call 'em names, Master Gaarge.'

'Goodbye, Betty, and make haste up to the Castle before all the small boys are poisoned. I can give you a lift, Sir,' said he to me, 'if you'll jump up behind.'

I thanked him, and got up behind, by the side of one of the other young gentlemen, who I thought didn't seem much to like having me there; and I felt very pleased, as we bowled along the Ridgeway, passing all the people who had been laughing at me and the donkey, that they should see that I was in such good company, and should be up at the Castle before any of them.

The whole Ridgeway was alive with holiday folk, some walking with their coats and bonnets off, some in great wagons, some in all sorts of strange vehicles, such as I had never seen before (many of which Master George declared had been impressed by Alfred's commissariat and hospital staff, in his wars against the Danes, when they were strong young traps); but from one and all there rose up a hum of broad Berkshire, and merry laughter, as we shot by them. Sometimes a yeoman in his gig, or on his stout hackney, would try to keep up with us, or to stop us from passing him, but Master George was a reckless driver, and somehow or another, galoping or trotting, on the right or the wrong, he *would* pass; so in about ten minutes we had got over the two miles of downs, and were close up to the Castle.

Here the first thing I saw was Joe, with two other farmers, carrying a lot of little white and pink flags, and measuring ground.

'Please put me down, Sir,' said I, 'there's my friend.'

'Ah, yes,' said Master George, pulling up, 'I see – you're staying with Farmer Hurst. Well, I'm much obliged to you for helping poor old Betty – she's a good struggling old widow body in our village; I've known her ever since I could walk and suck. Good morning, Mr Hurst; likely to be a good muster today.'

'Mornin', Sir,' said Joe, touching his hat, 'I think so – there's a smart lot of folk in the Castle already.'

'Well, I hope we may meet again,' said Master George to me, 'I won't forget the song for you,'– and away he drove towards the Castle.

'Why, Dick man, where's the old horse?' said Joe, looking as if I had come from the moon.

'Oh, I walked,' said I, 'I prefer it, when I have time.'

'Come own it, Dick,' said he, 'thou wast ashamed of the old horse's long rough coat – I didn't think thou hadst been such a dandy.'

'Upon my honour it was nothing of the sort,' said I, glad enough that he wasn't on the right scent.

'And how did you get along with one of our young squires?' said he.

'Oh, he offered me a lift,' said I; and then I told him my story.

'Well, you always seem to fall on your legs,' said he; 'who are they with him?'

'Oxford scholars, I think,' said I, 'from their talk; but I didn't get on much with them, they're not so free spoken as he is. But what are you about here, Joe?'

'Oh, helping the umpires to measure out the course for the cart-horse race,' said he; 'look, there are the flags right along for half a mile, and the finish is to be up there by the side of the Castle, for all the folk to see. But come along, for I must be after the umpires; I see they want me.'

'I think,' said I, 'I should like to go and see what's going on in the Castle.'

'Very good,' said he, 'then I'll look after you when we've done this job;' and away he went.

I wouldn't take time to go round by either of the entrances, but made straight across to the nearest point of the great earthworks, and scrambled over the outer bank, and down into the deep ditch, and up the inner bank, and stood there on the top, looking down on all the fun of the fair; for fair it was already, though it was very little past eleven o'clock in the morning.

There was the double line of booths and stalls which I had seen putting up the day before, making a long and broad street, and all decked out with nuts and apples, and ginger-bread, and all sorts of sucks and food, and children's toys, and cheap ribbons, knives, braces, straps, and all manner of gaudy-looking articles. Opposite, on the north side, all the shows had got their great pictures up of the wonders which were to be seen inside, and the performers were strutting about on the stage outside, and before one of them an acrobat was swinging backwards and forwards on the slack rope, and turning head over heels at the end of each swing. And every show had its own music, if it were only a drum and pan pipes, and all the musicians were playing, as loud as they could play, different tunes. Then, on the east side, were the great booths of the publicans, all decked out now with flowers and cheap flags, with their skittle-grounds behind; and lots of gipsies, and other tramps, with their 'three sticks a penny,' and other games. The west side was only occupied, as I said before, by the great white tent of the County Police, where the Committee were sitting, and Lord Craven's tents some way in front; but these looked pretty and gay now, for they had hoisted some good flags; and there in the middle stood the great ugly stage, and the greasy pole. The whole space was filled with all sorts of people, from ladies looking as if they had just come from Kensington Gardens, down to the ragged little gipsy children, with brown faces and brick-coloured hair, all moving about, and looking very much as if they were enjoying themselves. So after looking a minute, I got down into the crowd, and set to work to see everything I could.

I hadn't been pushing about amongst the rest above five minutes, when two men stopped close by me, one (who was the Wantage crier, I found out afterwards) with his hand full of papers, and the other carrying a gong, which he began to beat loud enough to deafen one. When the crowd had come round him, the crier began, and I should think he might have been heard at Elm Close:–

'Oh yes! oh yes! by order of the Committee, all persons who mean to play for prizes must enter their names on the umpires' lists. Oh yes! oh yes! the umpires' lists are open in the tent, and names may be entered from now till half-past twelve. Oh yes! a list of the umpires for the different games and sports may be seen on the board outside the tent-door. God save the Queen!'

As soon as he had done, he and the man with the gong went off to another part of the Castle, but I could see some of the men and boys, who had been standing round, sidling off toward the great tent to enter for some of the games, as I guessed. So I followed across the Castle to the space in front of the tent.

I could see, through the entrance, two or three of the Committee sitting at a table, with paper and pens and ink before them; and every now and then, from the little groups which were standing about, some man would make a plunge in, and go up to the table; and, after a word or two with them, would enter his name on one or more of the lists, and then come out, sometimes grinning, but generally looking as if he were half ashamed of himself. I remarked more and more through the day what a shy shamefaced fellow the real countryman was, while the gipsies and racing boys and tramps, who entered for the races, but not for the backsword or wrestling prizes, were all as bold as brass, and stood chattering away to the Committee-men till they were almost ordered out of the tent.

I sat down on the turf outside the tent to watch; for I felt very much interested in the games, and liked to see the sort of men who came to enter. There were not many very stout or tall men amongst them; I should say they averaged about eleven stone in weight, and five feet eight inches in height; but they looked a very tough race: and I could quite believe, while looking at them, what Joe told me one day – 'Though there's plenty of quicker men, and here and there stronger ones, scarce any man that ever comes down our way – either at navigator's work, or loafing about, like the gipsies and tramps – can ever come up to our chaps in *last,* whether at fighting or working.'

There was one man amongst them who struck me particularly, I suppose because he wore a Crimean medal with four clasps, and went quite lame on a crutch. I found out his history. Old Mattingly, the blacksmith of Uffington, had three sons when the Russian war broke out. They all went for soldiers. The first was shot through the hand, as that grey deadly dawn broke over Inkermann, on the 5th of November, 1854. Had he gone to the rear he would probably have lived. He fought till the last Russian vanished along the distant road, and over the bridge heaped with slain, like a gallant Berkshire lad – and then went to hospital and died of his wounds within a week. The second lies before Sebastopol in the advanced trenches of the right attack. The third, the young artilleryman, went through the whole war, and after escaping bayonet and shot and shell, was kicked by the horse of a wounded officer, and probably lamed for life. According to the rules of the service, my informant seemed to think, he was not entitled to a pension for life, 'but they had given him one for eighteen months after his discharge, so that he had almost a year of it to run; and perhaps he might learn blacksmith-work in that time, if he could stand at all, for that was mostly arm-work.'

I didn't know what the regulations as to pensions were, or how long young Mattingly would take to learn blacksmith-work, but I did feel rather ashamed that England couldn't afford to do a little more for such as he; and should be glad for my part to pay something towards it, if the Chancellor of the Exchequer, or somebody, would find out a way to set this right. Or perhaps if this should ever meet the eye of the Commander-in-chief, or of any of the gentlemen, who were made K.C.B.s in the war-time, or of any other person who had interest in the army, they may see whether anything more can be done for young Mattingly.

Many of the younger ones I could see hadn't made up their minds whether or no they should enter, and were larking and pushing one another about; and I saw several good trials of strength, and got an idea of what the wrestling was like before the lists were closed.

'Bi'st in for young geamsters prize at wrastlin', shepherd?' asked a young carter with his hat full of ribbons, of a tight-made neatly-dressed fellow, who had already won a second prize, I heard, at his village revel.

The shepherd nodded.

'Mose, mun,' went on the carter, 'thee shouldst go in. Thee bi'st big enough.'

Moses was as over-grown raw-boned fellow of about eighteen, in a short smock-frock and a pair of very dilapidated militia-trousers. He had been turning the matter over in his own mind for some time, and now, after looking the shepherd over for a minute, pulled his great hands out of his pockets, hunched up his shoulders, and grunted out –

''Zay! Try a file[2] wi' thee, shepherd.'

The bystanders all cheered. Moses, the militiaman, was rather a joke to them. The shepherd looked scornful, but was ready to try a file; but he stipulated that Mose must borrow some shoes instead of his great iron-clouted high-lows (no man is allowed to wrestle, I found, with any iron on his shoes).

This seemed likely to stop the fun. Moses pulled off his high-lows, and appeared in sinkers,[3] at which everybody roared; but no shoes were to be had. Then he offered to wrestle without shoes; but at last a pair were found, and Moses advanced with his great hands stretched out towards the shepherd, who, not deigning to take one hand out of his pocket, caught Mose's elbow with the other. After one or two awkward attempts, and narrowly escaping some well-meant trips, Mose bored in; and before the shepherd could seize the militiaman's collar with his second hand, over he went, and Mose was proclaimed winner of a file, amid shouts of laughter. Then they buckled to again, the shepherd doing his best; but somehow Mose managed to keep his legs; and when they went down, both fell on their sides, and it was only a dog-fall.

In another minute I saw the militiaman in the tent before the table. 'Plaze, Sur, put down Moses Tilling – young geamster – wrastlin'.'

After watching the tent till the lists were just closing, I started off to see if I could find Miss Lucy, who ought to have been up by this time, and to get something to eat before the sports began. The luncheon I managed easily enough, for I went over to the great booth in which I had dined the day before, and sat down at the long table, where Peter welcomed me, and soon gave me as much as I could eat and drink. But when I had finished, and went to look for my friends, I found it a very difficult business, and no wonder, for there were more than 20,000 people up on the Hill.

First I went to the outside of the Castle, where all the carriages were drawn up in long rows, to see if I could find the four-wheel amongst them. As I was poking about, I came close to a fine open carriage, and hearing a shout of merry laughter, looked up. There were a party at lunch; two ladies and some quite young girls inside, some boys on the box, and several gentlemen standing round, holding bottles and sandwiches; and they were all eating and drinking, and laughing at an old gipsy woman, who was telling the fortune of one of the ladies.

'Love'll never break your heart, my pretty lady,' said the old woman; 'let the Norwood gipsy see your hand, my pretty lady.'

The lady held out her right hand, and the little girls glanced at the lady, and one another, brimming with fun.

'It's the other hand the gipsy ought to see. Ah, well then, never mind,' she went on, as the lady looked quietly in her face, without moving a muscle, 'the old Norwood gipsy can read it all in your eyes.

There's a dark gentleman, and a light gentleman, who'll both be coming before long; there'll be sore hearts over it, but the richest will win before a year's out –' Here the girls clapped their hands, and burst into shouts, and the lady showed her other hand with a wedding ring on, and went on quietly with her lunch.

'Ah! I never said she wasn't married!' said the gipsy to the girls, who only laughed the more. I had got quite close up to the carriage, and at this moment caught the eye of the lady, who was laughing too; then I felt awkward all at once, and as if I was where I had no right to be. But she didn't look the least bit annoyed, and I was passing on, when I saw that Mr Warton was amongst the gentlemen on the other side of the carriage. 'Ah,' thought I, 'I wonder if he'll know me now he's with his fine friends?' But the next minute I was ashamed of myself for doubting, for I heard him wish them good-bye, and before I was ten yards from the carriage, he put his arm in mine.

'Well, you never rode after all,' he began.

'No, Sir,' said I. 'But where are they? I haven't seen Joe this two hours.'

'Oh, not far off,' said he; 'feeding, like the rest of us.'

And further down the line we found Joe, and Miss Lucy, and several friends of theirs, lunching on the turf by the four-wheel. So we sat down with them, but I didn't half like the way in which Miss Lucy was running on with two young farmers, one on each side of her. She told me afterwards that she had known them ever since they were children together, but somehow that didn't seem to me to mend the matter much. And then again, when Joe got up, and said it was time to move, for the sports would be just beginning, nothing would serve her but to walk off to Wayland Smith's cave. I wonder whether she did a little bit to provoke me; for she knew that I had been to see it the day before, and that I wanted particularly to see all the sports. But I don't think it could have been that after all, for when I said I should stay with Joe, she was just as pleasant as ever, and didn't seem to mind a bit whether I or any one else went with her or not.

I am afraid I shall make a very poor hand at telling about the sports, because I couldn't be in five or six places at once; and so I was kept running about, from the stage in the middle of the Castle out on to the downs to see the cart-horse race, and then back again into the Castle for the jingling match, and then out on the other side to the manger for the cheese races, and so on backwards and forwards; seeing the beginning of one sport, and the end of another, and the middle of a third. I wish the Committee would let the sports begin earlier, and then one might be able to see them all. However I must do the best I can, and just put down what I saw myself.

The first move for the sports was made a little before one, just as I got back into the Castle, after seeing Miss Lucy start for Wayland Smith's cave. The Committee came out of their tent in a body, each man carrying the lists of the entries for the sports over which he was to preside. But instead of going different ways, each to his own business, they walked across in a body to the stage, and stopped just underneath it, in the middle of a great crowd of men and boys; and then they shouted for silence, and the chairman spoke:–

'We wish to say a few words, my men, to those who are going to play with the sticks or wrestle today. There has been a good deal of talk about these sports, as you all know; and many persons think they shouldn't be allowed at all now-a-days – that the time for them has gone by. They say, that men always lose their tempers and get brutal at these sports. We have settled, however, to give the old-fashioned games a fair trial; and it will rest with yourselves whether we shall ever be able to offer prizes for them again. For, depend upon it, if there is any savage work today, if you lose your tempers, and strike or kick one another unfairly, you will never see any more wrestling or backswording on White Horse Hill. But we are sure we can trust you, and that there won't be anything to find fault with. Only remember again, you are on your trial, and the stage will be cleared at once, and no prizes given, if anything objectionable happens. And now, you can put to as soon as you like.'

The Committee then marched off, leaving a very large crowd round the stage, all eager for the play to begin.

The two umpires got up on to the stage, and walked round, calling out, 'Two old gamesters at backsword, and two old gamesters at wrastlin', wanted to put to.' But I suppose the chairman's speech had rather taken the men by surprise, for no one came forward, though there was a crowd twenty deep round the stage.

'Who are the old gamesters?' I asked of the man next to me.

'Them as has won or shared a first prize at any revel,' answered he, without looking round.

After a minute the chairman's brother, who didn't seem to have much scruple about these sports, jumped up on the stage, and blew an old French hunting-horn, till the young ones began to laugh; and then told the men not to be afraid to come up, for if they didn't begin at once there wouldn't be light to play out the ties.

At last there was a stir amongst the knot of Somersetshire men, who stood together at one corner of the stage; and one of them, stepping up, pitched on to it his stumpy black hat, and then climbed up after it himself, spoke a word to the umpires, and began handling the sticks, to choose one which balanced to his mind, while the umpires proclaimed, 'An old gamester wanted, to play with John Bunn of Wedmore.'

'There he stands, you see,' said Master George, who was close by me, though I hadn't seen him before, 'the only remaining representative of the old challenger at tourneys, ready to meet all comers. He ought to have a herald to spout out his challenge in verse. Why not?'

'I don't know what he could say more than the umpire has, Sir,' said I.

'He might blow his own trumpet at any rate,' said he; 'somehow thus;' and he repeated, after a false start or two:—

THE ZONG OF THE ZUMMERZETSHIRE OWLD GEAMSTER

Cham* a Zummerzetshire mun
  Coom here to hev a bit o'vun
Oo'lt** try a bout? I be'ant aveard
  Ov any man or mother's zun.

Cham a geamster owld and tough,
  Well knowed droo all the country zide,
And many a lusty Barkshire man
  To break my yead hev often tried.

Who's vor a bout o vriendly plaay
  As never should to anger move?
Zich spwoorts wur only meaned vor thaay
  As likes their mazzards broke for love.

* 'Cham' – 'I am,' a form still used in parts of Somersetshire.
** 'Oo'lt' – wilt thou.

John Bunn looked by no means a safe man to play with. He stood about five feet eleven, with spare long muscular limbs, a sallow complexion, and thick shock head of black hair, – a good defence in itself against any common blow of a stick. But now that the ice was broken, his challenge was soon answered; and George Gregory of Stratton, one of the best mowers in the Vale, appeared to uphold the honour of Berks and Wilts. He stood half a head shorter than his opponent, but was, probably, the stronger man of the two, and had a sturdy and confident look, which promised well, and was fair-haired, and, like David, ruddy to look upon.

While they were taking off coats and waistcoats, and choosing sticks, two wrestlers got up on the stage, and showed the shoes in which they were going to wrestle to the umpires, for approval; and stood at the ropes, ready to begin as soon as the first bout at backsword was over. The crowd drew a long breath, while Bunn and Gregory came forward, shook hands; and then throwing up their guards, met in the middle of the stage.

At the first rattle of the sticks, the crowd began cheering again, and pressed in closer to the stage; and I with them, for it was very exciting, *that* I felt at once. The coolness and resolution in the faces of the two men, as they struck and parried with those heavy sticks, trying all the points of each other's play in a dozen rapid exchanges; the skill and power which every turn of the wrist showed; and the absolute indifference with which they treated any chance blow which fell on arm or shoulder, made it really a grand sight; and with all my prejudices I couldn't help greatly admiring the players. 'Bout,' cried Bunn, after a minute or so, and down came their guards, and they walked to the side of the stage to collect their coppers from the crowd below in the baskets of their sticks, while the two first wrestlers put to in the middle.

I suppose there are more unsettled points in wrestling, or it is harder to see whether the men are playing fair, for the crowd was much more excited now than at the backsword play, a hundred voices shouting to the umpires every moment to stop this or that practice. Besides, the kicking, which is allowed at elbow and collar wrestling, makes it look brutal very often; and so I didn't like it so much as the backsword play, though the men were fine, good-tempered fellows, and, when most excited, only seemed to want what they called 'fair Doos.'

I stopped by the stage until Gregory had lost his head. How it happened I couldn't see, but suddenly the umpires cried out 'Blood!' The men stopped; Gregory put up his hand to his hair, found that the blood was really coming, and then dropped his stick and got down, quite as much surprised as I was. And two more old gamesters were called up, the first head being to Somersetshire.

But now I heard that the cart-horse race was just coming off, and so, following the crowd, made my way across to the east of the Castle.

I scrambled up to the highest part of the bank, and so got a capital view of the scene below. The course was marked out all the way down to the starting-post by rows of little pink and white flags, and the Committee-men were riding slowly up and down, trying to get the people to keep back behind the flags. The line was, on the whole, pretty well kept; but as the crowd got thicker every minute, every now and then a woman with two or three children would wander out to escape the pressure from behind; or a young couple keeping company would run across, hoping to better their position; or a lot of uproarious boys would start out for a lark, to try the tempers, and very possibly the whips, of the Committee.

Joe presently rode by the place where I was standing, and called out to me to come down and see the mounting. So I slipped out of the crowd, and ran down the back of the line to the starting place. There I found the Squire and the umpires, passing the men and horses. Five or six were all ready; the great horses in their thill harness, which jingled and rattled with every movement; and the carters perched up in the middle of the wood and leather and brass, in their white smock-frocks, with the brims of their break-of-days turned up in front, and a bunch of ribbons fluttering from the side, and armed with the regular long cart-whip. Just as I came up, Mr Avery Whitfield's bay horse, 'King of the Isle,' was passed, and took his place with the others. He was one of the three favourites, I heard people say.

'Call the next horse.'

'Mr Davenport's grey mare, Dairymaid,' shouts the umpire. Here she comes, with old Joe Humphries, the jockey and horse breaker, on her back. He is in full jockey costume – cap, jacket, and tops, with a racing whip and spurs. The umpires look doubtfully at him, and consult the Squire. At first they seem inclined not to let Joe ride at all, but as the owners of the other horses don't object, they only insist on his taking off his spurs and changing his whip for a common long carter's whip. Then Dairymaid is passed, and then one other horse; eight in all. Two of the Committee gallop down in front to clear the course for the last time; the word 'Off' is given; and away go the great steeds in furious plunging gallop, making the whole hill shake beneath them, and looking (as I heard one of the Oxford scholars remark) like a charge of German knights in some old etching. Close after them came the umpires, the Committee-men, and all the mounted farmers, cheering and shouting pieces of advice to the riders; and the crowd, as they pass, shout and wave their hats, and then rush after the horses. How everybody isn't killed, and how those men can sit those great beasts in the middle of that rattling mass of harness, were my puzzles, as I scrambled along after the rest.

Meantime, in the race, Dairymaid shoots at once some yards ahead, and improves her lead at every stride; for she is a famous mare, and old Joe Humphries understands the tricks of the course, and can push her and lift her in ways unknown to the honest carters and foggers, who come lumbering behind him – Joe even has time for a contemptuous glance over his shoulder at his pursuers. But the race is not always to the swift, at least not to those who are swiftest at starting. Half-way up the course, Dairymaid ceases to gain; then she shows signs of distress, and scarcely answers to old Joe's persuasions. 'King of the Isle' is creeping up to her – the carter shakes his bridle, and begins to ply his long cart-whip – they are crossing the Ridgeway, where stand the carter's fellow-servants, Mr Whitfield's fogger, shepherd, plough-boys, &c., who set up a shout as he passes, which sends the bay right up abreast of the mare. No wonder they are excited, for the master has promised that the three guineas, the price of the new thill harness, shall be divided between them, if the bay wins.

In another fifty yards he is drawing ahead. All old Joe's efforts are in vain; hs jockeyship has only done him harm, whereas the carter's knowledge of what his steed's real powers are, has been the making of him, and he rides in, brandishing his long cart-whip, an easy winner.

Dairymaid is second, but only just before the ruck; and old Joe creeps away, let us hope, a humbler and a wiser man.

Of course I couldn't see all this myself, because I was behind, but Joe told me all about the race directly afterwards. When I got up there was a great crowd round 'King of the Isle,' from whose back the carter was explaining something about the race. But I couldn't stay to listen, for I heard that the races for the 'prime coated Berkshire fives' (as they called the cheese), were just coming off; so I hurried away to the brow of the hill, just above the Horse, where it is steepest; for I wanted of all things to see how men could run down this place, which I couldn't get up without using both hands.

There stood Mr William Whitfield, of Uffington, the umpire who had to start the race, in his broad brimmed beaver, his brown coat and waistcoat with brass buttons, and drab breeches and gaiters. I thought him a model yeoman to look at, but I didn't envy him his task. Two wild-looking gipsy women, with their elf-locks streaming from under their red handkerchiefs, and their black eyes flashing, were rushing about amongst the runners, trying to catch some of their relations who were going to run; and screaming out that their men should never break their limbs down that break-neck place. The gipsies dodged about, and kept out of their reach, and the farmer remonstrated, but the wild women still persevered. Then, losing all patience, he would turn and poise the wheel, ready to push it over the brow, when a shout from the bystanders warns him to pause, and, a little way down the hill, just in the line of the race, appear two or three giggling lasses, hauled along by their sweethearts, and bent on getting a very good view. Luckily at this moment the Chairman appeared, and rode his white horse down in front of the line of men, where there seemed to me to be footing for nothing but a goat. Then the course was cleared for a moment, he moved out of the line, making a signal to the farmer, who pushed the wheel at once over the brow, and cried, 'Off.' The wheel gained the road in three bounds, cleared it in a fourth monster bound which measured forty yards, and hurried down far away to the bottom of the manger, where the other two umpires were waiting to decide who is the winner of the race.

Away go the fourteen men in hot pursuit, gipsies, shepherds, and light-heeled fellows of all sorts, helter-skelter; some losing their foothold at once, and rolling or slipping down; some still keeping their footing, but tottering at every step; one or two, with their

bodies well thrown back, striking their heels firmly into the turf, and keeping good balance. They are all in the road together, but here several fall on their faces, and others give in; the rest cross it in a moment, and are away down the manger. Here the sheep-walks, which run temptingly along the sides of the manger, but if they would look forward will take the runners very little nearer the bottom where the wheel lies, mislead many; and amongst the rest, the fleetest of the gipsies, who makes off at full speed along one of them. Two or three men go still boldly down the steep descent, falling and picking themselves up again; and Jonathan Legg, of Childrey, is the first of these. He has now gained the flat ground at the bottom, where after a short stagger he brings himself up, and makes straight for the umpires and the wheel. The gipsy now sees his error; and turning short down the hill, comes into the flat, running some twenty yards behind Jonathan. In another hundred yards he would pass him, for he gains at every stride; but it is too late; and we, at the top of the hill, cheer loudly when we see Jonathan, the man who had gone straight all the way, touch the wheel a clear ten yards before his more active rival.

I should have liked to have seen the boys' races down the manger, but was afraid of missing some other sport, so I left farmer Whitfield at his troublesome post, shouting out the names of the boys and trying to get them into line, and went back into the Castle, where I found a crowd round the greased pole; and when I got up to it, saw a heavy-looking fellow, standing some five feet up the pole, with one foot in a noose of cord depending from a large gimlet, and the other leg hooked round the pole. He held in his right hand another large gimlet, which he was preparing to screw into the pole to support a second noose, and gazed stolidly down at a Committee-man, who was objecting 'that this wasn't fair climbing – that if gimlets and nooses were to be allowed, he could get up himself.' I thought he was right; but public feeling seemed to side with the climber; so the Committee-man gave in, declaring that there would be no more legs of mutton to climb for, if anything but arms and legs were to be used.

'Rather a slow bit of sport this,' I said to an old grey-headed man, who was leaning on his stick at my side, and staring up at the performer.

'Ees, Zur,' answered he, 'I dwon't knaow but what it be.'

'Do you call it fair climbing, now?'

'Auh, bless'ee, not I. I minds seein' the young chaps when I wur a buoy, climin' maypowls a deal higher nor that, dree at a time. But now-a-days 'um be lazy, and afraid o' spwiling their breeches wi' the grase.'

'Are there any maypoles about here now?'

'Never a one as I knows on, Zur, for twenty mile round. The last as I remembers wur the Longcott one, and Parson Watts of Uffington had he sawed up nigh forty year ago, for fear lest there should ha' been some murder done about 'um.'

'Murder about a maypole! Why, how was that?'

'Auh! you see, Zur, this here Longcott maypowl wur the last in all these parts, and a wur the envy of a zight o' villages round about. Zo, one cluttery[4] night in November, thirty of our Ashbury chaps thay started down to Longcott, and dug 'un up, and brought 'un cler away on handspikes, all the waay to the Crown'd Inn at Ashbury, and 'tis quite vour mil'd.'

'On handspikes! Why, how big was he, then?'

'Auh! a fyeightish sized 'un. How big? whoy a sight bigger bless'ee, nor that 'un, and all the bottom half on 'un solid oak. When thay cum to put 'un up afore the bar winder of the Crown'd, a reached right up auver the tops o' the housen. But zoon arter a wur put up, the Uffington chaps cum up, and tuk and carried 'un down ther'. Ther' was a smartish row or two about 'un at Uffington arter that, but they watched 'un night and day; and when the Lambourn chaps cum arter 'un one night, they chucked scaldin' water right auver'm. Zo then Parson Watts, he tuk and sawed 'un up, and guv 'un to the owld women at Christmas for virewood.'

I walked away from the pole, turning over in my mind whether Parson Watts was right or wrong in his summary method of restoring peace to his parish, and, somehow or other, found myself again close under the stage. Now, and throughout the day, I found no flagging there; whenever I passed there was the crowd of men standing round, and the old and young gamesters hard at work. So I began to believe what Joe had said, that the countrymen thought more about these games than anything else, and wouldn't care to go to the pastime if they were stopped.

I found that the Ashbury men were carrying it all their own way in the wrestling, and that their champion, old Richens (the rat-catcher, and old gamester in his fiftieth year), would probably not even have to wrestle at all; for his own men were throwing all the gamesters of the other parishes, and of course would give up to him when it came to the last ties. The men all wrestle in sides, at least the old gamesters do; so that a man generally plays for his parish, and not for his own head, which is a better thing, I think.

As to the backsword play, the stage was strewed with splinters of sticks and pieces of broken baskets, and many a younger gamester has had his first broken head in public. But, for the chief prize, matters are going hard with Berks and Wilts. The Somersetshire old gamesters have won two heads to one; and, as they have six men in, and Berks and Wilts only four, the odds are all in favour of the cider county, and against the beer drinkers.

In good time up gets an old gamester, who looks like the man to do credit to the royal county. It is Harry Seeley, of Shrivenham, the only Berkshire man in; for there has been some difference between Berks and Wilts, and Harry's two mates haven't entered at all. So he, being one of the true bull-dog breed, is in for his own head, against all odds, and is up to play the next Somersetshire man.

Harry is a fine specimen of an Englishman. Five feet eight high, with a bullet head, and light blue eyes; high-couraged, cool, and with an absolutely imperturbable temper. He plays in a blue shirt, thin from age and wear, through which you may see the play of his splendid arms and chest. His opponent is a much younger man, about the same size; but a great contrast to Harry, for he has a savage and sly look about him.

They shake hands, throw themselves into position, and the bout begins. Harry is clearly the finer player, and his adversary feels this at once; and the shouts of anticipated victory, in the Berkshire tongue, rouse his temper.

Now comes a turn of the savage play, which ought never to be seen on a stage. The Somerset man bends far back, and strikes upper cuts at the face and arms, and then savagely at the body. He is trying to maim and cow, and not to win by fair brave play. The crowd soon begin to get savage too; upper-cutting is not thought fair in Berks and Wilts; a storm begins to brew, hard words are bandied, and a cry of 'Foul,' and 'Pull him down,' is heard more than once, and the Committee man, who watches from below, is on the point of stopping the bout.

But nothing puts out old Harry Seeley; no upper cut can reach his face, for his head is thrown well back, and his guard is like a rock; and though the old blue shirt is cut through and through, he makes no more of the welts of the heavy stick than if it were a cat's tail. Between the bouts his face is cheery and confident, and he tells his friends to 'hold their noise, and let him alone to tackle the chap,' as he hands round his basket for the abounding coppers.

Now I could see well enough why the parsons don't like these games. It gave me a turn, to watch the faces round the stage getting savage, and I could see what it might soon get to if there was much of this wild work. And there were Master George, and the two Oxford scholars, at the opposite corner of the stage, shouting till they were hoarse for old Seeley, and as savage and wicked-looking as any of the men round them; setting such a bad example, too as I thought, – whereas it didn't matter for a fellow like me, who was nobody, – so I shouted, and threw my coppers to old Seeley, and felt as wild as any of them, I do believe. Three bouts, four bouts pass; Harry's stick gets in oftener and oftener. Has the fellow no blood in him? There it comes at last! In the fifth bout, Harry's stick goes flashing in again, a fair down blow from the wrist, which puts the matter beyond all question, as the Somersetshire man staggers back across the stage, the blood streaming from under his hair. Loud are the shouts which greet the fine-tempered old gamester, as he pulls on his velveteen coat, and gets down from the stage.

'Why, Harry, thou'dst broke his yead second bout, mun, surely!' shout his admirers.

'No,' says Harry, dogmatically, 'you see, mates, there's no 'cumulation of blood belongs to thay cider-drinking chaps, as there does to we as drinks beer. Besides, they drinks vinegar allus for a week afore playin', which dries up most o' the blood as they *has* got; so it takes a 'mazin' sight of cloutin' to break their yeads as should be.'

After this bout all the other play seemed to be tasteless; so, promising myself to come back and see the ties played off (unless Miss Lucy turned up in the meantime, in which case I shouldn't have dared to go near the stage, and in fact I felt rather nervous already lest she should have seen or heard of me there), I marched off, and joined the crowd which was collecting round the jingling ring. That crowd was one of the pleasantest sights of the whole day. The jingling match seemed a very popular sport, especially with the women. There they were, of all ranks – for I'm certain I saw some young ladies in riding habits, and others in beautiful muslins, whom I, and Jem Fisher, and little Neddy have often seen riding down to Rotten Row on summer evenings – seated on the grass or standing round the ring, in all sorts of dresses, from fine silks down to cottons at 2*d*. a yard, and all looking pleasant and good tempered, and as if they were quite used to being mixed up like this every day – which I'm sure I wish they were, for my part, especially if the men were allowed to join in the crowd too, as we were round the jingling ring. For there were gentlemen, both parsons and others, and farmers, and ploughboys, and all manner of other men and boys.

I don't know what sort of fun a jingling match is in general, but I thought this one much the slowest game I saw. The ring must have been forty yards across, or thereabouts, and there were only eight blindfolded men running after the bellman. To make it good fun there should have been twenty-five or thirty at least. Then the bellman, who has his hands tied behind him, ought to have the bell tied round his neck, or somewhere where he can't get at it to stop the ringing; but our bellman had the bell tied to his waistband behind, so that he could catch hold of it with his hands, and stop it when he was in danger. Then half the men could see, I'm sure, by the way they carried their heads up in the air, especially one gipsy, who, I think, won the prize at last. The men who couldn't see were worth watching, for they kept catching and tumbling over one another. One time they made a rush to the rope, just where some of the young ladies were sitting, and, as nearly as could be, tumbled over among them. I thought there would have been a great scrambling and screaming; not a bit of it – they never flinched an inch, or made the least cry, and I was very proud to think they were my countrywomen. After the bellman had been caught about a minute, there was a great laugh at one of the blinded men, who made a rush, and caught a Committee-man, who was standing in the ring, in his arms. But on the whole I thought the game a poor one, and was glad when it was over.

I hurried away directly after the jingling match, and went across the Castle, and out on to the down where the cart-horse race had been run to see the foot-races, which were run over the last half of the same course, on which ten good stiff sets of hurdles at short distances apart had been set up. I found a debate going on between the umpires and some of the men as to whether they were all to start together. The regular agricultural labourers were remonstrating as to some of the candidates.

'It beant narra moussel o' use for we chaps to start along wi' thay light-heeled gentry,' said one, – 'Whoy, look 'ee here, zur's one, and yander's another, wi' a kind o' dancin' pumps on, and that 'un at tother end wi' a cricketin' waistcut.'

'And there's two o' them little jockey chaps amongst 'em, sumweres, Zur,' said another, looking about for these young gentlemen, who dodged behind some of the bigger candidates.

'How can we help that?' said the umpire.

'Auh, Zur, thay be all too nimble by half for we to be of any account to 'em,' persisted the first speaker. 'If twur for the sticks now, or wrastling –'

'Well, but what shall we do then?' interrupted the umpire.

'Let I pick out ten or a dozen on 'em to run by theirselves.' The umpires proposed this to the rest, and, no one objecting, told Giles the protester to pick out the ten he was most afraid of. This Giles proceeded to do with a broad grin on his face, and generally seemed to make a good selection. But presently he arrived at, and after a short inspection passed over, a young fellow in his blue shirt sleeves and a cloth cap, who to the umpire's eye seemed a dangerous man.

'Why, Giles,' said he, 'you're never going to pass him over?'

'Auh, ees, Zur,' said Giles, 'let he 'bide along wi' we chaps. Dwont'ee zee, he's a tipped and naayled 'un?'

When Giles had finished his selection, the first lot were started, and made a grand race; which was won by a Hampshire man from Kingsclere, the second man, not two feet behind, being a young Wiltshire farmer, who, having never been beaten in his own neighbourhood, had come to lose his laurels honourably at the Scouring.

The running in the second race was, of course, not so good, but much more amusing. The 'tipped and naayled 'uns' were a rushing lot, but very bad at rising. Hurdle after hurdle went down before them with a crash, and the most wonderful summersaults were executed. The second hurdle finished poor Giles, who charged it manfully, and found himself the next moment on his broad back, gazing placidly up into the evening sky. The cloth cap, notwithstanding his shoes, went easily ahead, and won in a canter. I heard one of the umpires rallying Giles afterwards at his want of eyes.

'Ees, Zur,' said Giles, hunching up his great shoulders, 'I wur tuk in, zure enough. He wur a town chap arter all, as wouldn't ha' knowed a piece o' clumpers afore he cum across to White Hos Hill.'

I left the umpires now to start the other races, and got back once again into the Castle. I was now beginning to get very tired in my legs, though not in my spirits, so I went and sat down outside the crowd, which was thicker than ever round the stage, for the ties were being played out. I could hear the umpire call every now and then for some gamester who was not forthcoming to play out his tie – 'John Giles, if you beant on the stage in five minutes, to put to with James Higgins, you shall lose your head' – through all the cheers and shouts, which rose louder and louder now that every blow or trip might decide the prizes. And while I was sitting, the donkey races were run outside, and I heard were good fun; especially the last one, in which no man rode his own donkey, and the last donkey had the prize. I hope my friend, the old suck-woman, entered neighbour Thorne's beast, for if she did I'll be bound he carried off the prize for her. They were the only sports that I didn't manage to see something of.

It was now just five o'clock, the hour for the pig-race, which seemed to be a most popular sport, for most of the lookers-on at the stage went off to see it, leaving only a select crowd of old and young gamesters, most of whom had been playing themselves, and whom nothing could drag five yards from the posts until the ties were all played out. I was just considering whether I should move or stay where I was, when Master George came striding by and caught sight of me.

'Hullo,' said he, 'how is it you're not on the move? You must see the pig-race; come along.' So I got up and shambled along with him.

The pig was to be started on the slope below the west entrance, where the old gentleman had stood and lectured me the day before about Earl Sidroc. There was the spring cart, covered with a net, with a fine young Berkshire pig in it, just at the place where the Bersirkir (as he called them) made their last stand. When we came up, the runners, thirty in number, with their coats and waistcoats off, were just being drawn up in line inside the Castle, from which place they were to be started, and run down through the west entrance out on to the open down, at the word 'off.' It was thought that this rush down between the double banks, covered thickly with the crowd, would be the finest sight of the race. But the rush never came. Piggy was to have five minutes law, and the Committee-man who went down to turn him out put his snout towards Ashdown Park, and gave him a push in hopes that he would take straight away over the downs, and so get a good start. Of course, he turned right round and came trotting and grunting up towards the Castle, to see what all the bustle could be about. Then the crowd began to shout at him, and to press further and further down the outer earthworks, though all the Committee were there to keep the course clear for the regular runners; and at last, before half of the five minutes were over, the whole line broke up with a great shout, and the down was covered in a moment with countless men and boys in full chase of Piggy. Then the lawful candidates could stand it no longer, and away they went too, cleaving their way through the press, the Committee riding after them as fast as was safe in such a crowd, to see fair play if possible at the finish.

In a minute or two, Piggy was mobbed, surrounded, seized first by one of the crowd, and then by a lawful runner. These tumbled over in their struggle without loosing their hold and more of their friends over them, and from the middle of the mass poor Piggy sent up the most vigorous and dismal squeals, till the Committee-men rode in, laying about with their whips; and Farmer Whitfield, springing off, seized Piggy, and in another minute was cantering away with him towards Wayland Smith's cave. Here he was turned out again for a fair race, and was won by Charles Ebury of Fernham; who, fearing the results of his racing performances, sold him at once for 10s. to the Woolston carrier. But I am happy to say that he wasn't really hurt, for I went to see him some days afterwards, and found him as hearty as pig could be.

Master George and I agreed, as we walked back to the Castle, that it is a shame to have a pig-race.

'No,' said he, 'let men run any risk they like of broken heads or limbs for themselves; they may play or not as they like. But Piggy has no choice, and to let him run the risk of having the legs pulled out of his body before he is wanted for pork, isn't fair.'

'He didn't seem to think it was, certainly, Sir,' I said.

'No,' said he, laughing; 'did you ever hear such a song as he made?

No animal can talk like a pig. He can scold or remonstrate just as well as a Christian. Any one who knows the language can tell you just what he is saying. Well,' he went on, 'I see you don't believe me; now I will go and hear what he has to say about this proceeding, and give you it word for word.'

This was what he gave me afterwards, with the other songs he had promised me:–

THE LAY OF THE HUNTED PIG

Vathers, mothers, mothers' zons!
You as loves yer little wuns!
Happy pegs among the stubble,
Listen to a tale of trouble;
Listen, pegs in yeard and stye,
How the Berkshire chaps zard I.

I wur barn at Kingstone-Lisle,
Wher I vrolicked var a while,
As vine a peg as e'er wur zeen
(One of a litter o' thirteen)
Till zome chaps wi' cussed spite
Aimed ov I to make a zite,
And to have a 'bit o' vun,'
Took I up to Uffington.

Up, vorights* the Castle mound
They did zet I on the ground;
Then a thousand chaps, or nigh,
Runned and hollered arter I –
Ther, then, I, till I wur blowed,
Runned and hollered all I knowed,
When, zo zure as pegs is pegs,
Eight chaps ketched I by the legs,
Two to each – 'tis truth I tell 'ee –
Dree more clasped I round the belly!
Under all they fellows lyin' –
Pegs! – I thought as I wur dyin'.

But the Squire (I thenks I zee un),
Varmer Whitfield ridin' wi' un,
Fot I out o' all thuck caddle,
Stretched athurt the varmer's zaddle –
Bless 'em, pegs in yeard and stye,
Them two vrends as stuck to I.

Barkshire men, vrom Hill and Vale,
All as ever hears this tale,
If to spwoort you be inclined,
Plaze to bear this here in mind –
Pegs beant made no race to win,
Be zhart o' wind, and tight o' skin,
Dwont 'ee hunt 'em, but instead
At backswyrd break each other's yead
Cheezes down the manger rowl –
Or try and clim the greasy powl.

Pegs! in stubble yeard and stye,
May you be never zard like I,
Nor druv wi greasy ears and tail,
By men and bwoys drough White Horse Vale.

* 'Vorights' – opposite.

CHAPTER VII

W.J. LINTON

ASTER George slipped away from me somehow, after the pig-race, so I strolled up into the Castle again. The sports were all over, so the theatres and shows were making a greater noise than ever, but I didn't feel inclined to go to any of them, and kept walking slowly round the bank on the opposite side, and looking down at the fair. In a minute or two I heard cheering, and saw an open carriage, with postilions, driving out of the Castle, and three or four young ladies and a gentleman or two cantering along with it. I watched them for some way across the downs, and thought how nice it must be to be able to ride well, and to have nice horses to go galloping over the springy downs, into the golden sunset, putting up the larks and beautiful little wheatears; and, besides all that, to have all the people cheering one too! So down I went into the crowd, to find out who they were. It was Lord Craven and his party, the first man I came across told me; and then I quite understood why this carriage should be the only one to come inside the Castle, and why the people should cheer; because, you see, the White Horse, and Dragons' Hill, and the Manger, all belong to him, and he is very good-natured in letting everybody go there and do pretty much what they please. There were other carriages going off now from the row outside, and coachmen bringing up their horses to harness, and a few of the foot people who came from the longest distances, starting along the Ridgeway, or down the Uffington Road. I was standing watching all this, and thinking how I was to find my party, and whether I should go behind in the four-wheel (which I began to feel very much inclined to do, for I was getting tired, and it would be dark), when I saw Joe bustling about amongst the crowd, and looking out for some one; so I made across to him.

'Ah, there you are,' said he, as soon as he caught sight of me, 'I've been hunting for you; it's all over for today. Lu sent me after you to come and have some tea. If you like, you can go home directly afterwards with her and Mr Warton.'

I was very pleased to hear that Miss Lucy had sent after me, but I didn't want to show it.

'What are you going to do?' said I.

'Oh,' said Joe, 'I shan't leave till all the Committee go: I must be at the giving away of the prizes in the tent; and then, if anything should happen afterwards – any row, you know, or that sort o' thing – I shouldn't like to be gone.'

I didn't say anything more, as I thought I might just as well leave it open; so I followed him to the west side of the Castle, where the police tent stood, and it was quite quiet.

'Here they are,' said Joe, 'over in the ditch;' and he scrambled up the bank, and I after him, and in the ditch below sure enough was a most cozy tea-party. Miss Lucy, with her bonnet off, was sitting cutting up a cake, and generally directing. Two other young women, nice fresh-looking girls, but not to be named with her, were setting out a few cups and saucers and plates, which they had borrowed from some of the stalls. Mr Warton was on his knees with his hat off, blowing away till he was red in the face at a little fire made of chips and pieces of old hampers, over which the kettle, also borrowed, hung from three sticks driven into the ground so that their tops met above the fire. Two or three young farmers sat about looking on, or handing things as they were wanted, except one impudent young fellow of about eighteen, with scarcely a hair on his chin, who was almost in Miss Lucy's pocket, and was meddling with everything she was doing.

'Well, here you are, at last,' said she, looking up at us; 'why, where have you been all day?'

'I am sure I have been hunting after you very often,' said I, which, perhaps, was rather more than I ought to have said; 'but it isn't easy for one who is a stranger to find people in such a crowd.'

'I don't know that,' said she, with a pretty little toss of her head; 'where there's a will there's a way. If I hadn't found friends, I might have been alone all day – and there are three or four of the shows I have never seen, now.'

I began to look as sorry as I could, while I thought what to answer, when the young man who was close to her tried to steal some of the cake; she turned round quickly, and rapped his fingers with the back of her knife, and he pretended to be hurt. She only laughed, and went on cutting up the cake, but she called him Jack, and seemed so intimate with him that it put me out, and I sat down on the other side of the circle, some way off.

'It's all right,' said the Parson, looking up from the fire; 'boils splendidly – give me the tea.'

Miss Lucy handed him a little parcel of tea from her bag, and he put it into the kettle.

'I declare we have forgotten the milk,' said she, 'do run and fetch it, Jack – it's in a bottle under the back seat of the four-wheel.'

I jumped up before Jack, who hardly moved, and ran off to fetch the milk; for which she gave me a pleasant smile when I came back, and I felt better pleased, and enjoyed the tea and cake and bread and butter, and all the talk over it, very much; except that I couldn't stand this Jack, who was forcing her to notice him every minute, by stealing her teaspoon or her cake, or making some of his foolish remarks.

The sun set splendidly before we had finished, and it began to get a little chilly.

'Well,' said Joe, jumping up, 'I'm off to get the horse put to. You'd better be starting, Lu; you won't be down hill much before dark, now, and there's no moon – worse luck.'

'Very well,' said she, taking up her bonnet, and putting it on; 'we shall be ready in five minutes.'

'You'll go behind with them, I suppose,' said Joe to me.

'I'm to have a seat, mind,' struck in that odious Jack; 'Lucy promised me that an hour ago.' I could have given him a good kick; however, I don't think I showed that I was put out.

'How can you tell such fibs, Jack?' said she; but I didn't take any notice of that.

'Thank you, I wish to stay on the hill,' said I. 'Besides, the four-wheel will be full without me.'

She didn't seem to hear; and began talking to one of the other girls.

'But how are you to get down?' said Joe.

'Oh, I can walk,' said I, 'or ride behind you.'

'Very good, if you like,' said he; 'the chestnut would carry six, if her back was long enough;' and away he went to get the four-wheel ready.

We followed; Miss Lucy sticking close to her friend, and never saying a word to any of us. I walked with Mr Warton, who was in the highest spirits, looking over his shoulder, and raving about the green tints in the sunset.

When we got to the carriages, there was kissing and shaking of hands, and the rest went off, while the parson and Miss Lucy packed into the front seat, and Jack and Jem the carter-boy into the hind seat of the four-wheel; and away they drove, wishing us 'good night.' I watched them for some time, and could see Jack leaning forward close to her ear; and turned back with Joe into the Castle, more out of sorts than I had been since I left London.

Joe hurried off to the police tent, where the Committee were giving away the prizes, saying I should find him there when I wanted him; and I loitered away to see whatever was to be seen. At first nothing seemed to please me. I watched the men and boys playing at three sticks a penny, and thought I might as well have been on Primrose Hill. Then I went and looked at the shows; and there was the fellow in flesh-coloured tights, turning over and over on the slack rope, and the clarionet and French horn and drum, played by the three men in corduroys, all out of tune, and louder than ever, as if they had only just begun, instead of having been screaming and rumbling away all day; and the man outside the pink-eyed lady's caravan was shouting away for the hundredth time all about her, and then playing the pan-pipes, as if no other woman in the world had pink eyes.

I was determined they shouldn't have any of my money at any rate, so I strolled further down the line, and looked into a low booth where a fiddle was going. Here several couples were dancing, with their arms a-kimbo, on some planks which had been put down on the grass, and all the rest of the booth was crowded with others looking on. This pleased me better, for the dancers seemed to enjoy themselves wonderfully, and made a sort of clattering accompaniment to the music with their hob-nailed shoes, which was merry and pleasant.

When I was tired of watching them I thought I would go and find Joe; so I went over to the tent, and there I got all right, and began to enjoy myself again.

In the further corner of the tent the Squire and another justice were sitting, and hearing a charge of pocket picking, of which there were only two during the whole day, the police told me. Opposite the door, the rest of the Committee were sitting at a table and giving away the prizes.

Joe beckoned me in, and I went round to the back of the table and looked on. As the men came up from the group round the door, when their names were called out, the umpires said a few words to each of them and then gave them their prizes, and most of them made some sort of speech in answer; for they were much less shy than in the morning, I suppose from the sense of having earned their right to hold up their heads by winning. The owner of the successful donkey was just carrying out the flitch of bacon when I arrived; after him the Somersetshire backsword players were called in to take the first three prizes for that sport, they having beaten all the Wiltshire men; while old Seeley, the only Berkshire man entered, to everybody's surprise had not played out his tie, but had given his head (as they said) to his second opponent. Therefore, although entitled to the last prize for having won his first bout, he had not done all his duty in the eyes of the umpires, who gently complained, while handing him over his four half-crowns, and wondered that so gallant an old gamester, and a Vale man, should not have played out his ties for the honour of the county.

'Well, gen'l'men,' said old Seeley, giving a hitch with his shoulders, 'I'll just tell you how it was. You see, ther wur six Somersetshire old gamesters come up to play, and ther wur six of our side to play 'em: dree Wiltshire and dree Berkshire, if so be as we could have made a party. But the dree from Wiltshire they wouldn't go in along wi' we, and turned their backs on me and my two mates; so my two mates wouldn't go in at all, and wanted me to give out too. But you see, gen'l'men, I'd a spent a matter of a pound over getting myself a little better food, and making myself lissom; so thinks I, I must go up and have a bout, let it be how t'wool. And you saw, gen'l'men, as I played a good stick. When it cum' to playing off the

ties, there wur dree Somersetshire tiers, and two of our side, that's
Slade and me. But when a man turns his back on me, gen'l'men, why
I turns my back on him; so I guv my head to young Mapstone, and
left Slade to win if he could. Though I thinks, if thay Wiltshire
chaps had behaved theirselves as thay should, we might ha' had the
prize, for I knows as I never played freer in my life. And I hopes,
gen'l'men, as you don't think I wur afeared of any man as ever got on
that stage. Bless you!' said old Seeley, warming up, 'I be that fond o'
thay sticks, I assure you, gen'l'men, I'd as lief meet a man as is a man
for a bout wi' thay sticks, as I would – a joint of roast beef.'

Old Seeley's speech carried conviction, for there could be no
mistake about the tone in which he drew his last comparison, after a
moment's pause to think of the thing he liked best, and he retired
from the tent in high favour, as I think he deserved to be.

After watching these doings for some time I began to feel very
hungry, for I had eaten hardly anything at tea, so I told Joe that he
would find me over in the great booth getting some supper, and went
out. It was getting quite dark, and the stage and poles looked black
and melancholy as I passed by them. But the publicans' booths were
all lighted up inside and looked very cheerful, and were full of
holiday folk, fortifying themselves with all sorts of meat and drink
before starting for the descent of the hill and the walk home in the
dark.

I pushed my way through the crowd round the door, and reached
the bar, where the landlord recognised me directly and handed me
over to Peter, who soon landed me at the table in the recess, which
was still well supplied with cold joints and bread and cheese. While
he went off to get my plate and ale, I had time to look round. The
booth was much gayer than the day before; every post was decked
more or less with flowers and evergreen, and the flags had been
brought inside. The whole place was lighted with dips and flickering
oil lamps, which gave light enough to let one see all parts of the tent
pretty clearly.

There were a good many tables ranged about; the one nearest to
ours wasn't yet occupied, but at all the others were groups of men
drinking beer, and some smoking and talking eagerly over the events
of the day. Those nearest the high table seemed under some little
restraint, and spoke low; but from the farther tables rose a loud hum
of the broadest Berkshire, and an occasional scrap of a song. A few

women were scattered here and there – mostly middle-aged, hard-working housewives – watching their good men, and anxious to carry them off in good time, and before too much of the harvest-savings had found its way to the landlord's till. About the entrance was a continually-changing crowd, and the atmosphere of the whole was somewhat close, and redolent of not very fragrant tobacco.

At the supper-table where I was were seven or eight men. The one just opposite me was a strong-built, middle-aged man, in a pepper-and-salt riding-coat and waistcoat, with an open, weather-beaten face, and keen, deep-set eyes, who seemed bent on making a good supper. Next above him were the two Oxford scholars, but they didn't take the least notice of me, which I thought they might have done, after our morning's ride together. They had finished supper, and were smoking cigars, and chatting with one another, and with the pepper-and-salt man, whom they called Doctor. But my observations were soon cut short by Peter, who came back with my plate and knife and fork, and a foaming pewter of ale, and I set to work as heartily as the Doctor himself.

'You'll find some of this lettuce and water-cress eat well with your beef, Sir,' said he, pushing across a dish.

'Thank you, Sir,' said I; 'I find that watching the games makes one very hungry.'

'The air, Sir, all the downs air,' said the Doctor; 'I call them Doctor Downs. Do more for the appetite in six hours than I can in a week. Here, Peter, get this gentleman some of your mistress's walnut pickles.'

And then the good-natured Doctor fell to upon his beef again, and chatted away with the scholars and me, and soon made me feel myself quite at home. I own that I had done my neighbours a little injustice; for they were pleasant enough when the ice was broken, and I daresay didn't mean to be rude after all.

As soon as I had finished my supper, the shorter of the scholars handed me a large cigar, the first whiff of which gave me a high idea of the taste of my contemporaries of the upper classes in the matter of tobacco.

Just then the verse of a song, in which two or three men were joining, rose from the other end of the tent, from amidst the hum of voices.

'I wish those fellows would sing out,' said the short scholar; 'I can't make out more than a word or two.'

'You wouldn't be any the wiser if you could,' said the other; 'we have ceased to be a singing nation. The people have lost the good old ballads, and have got nothing in their place.'

'How do you know?' said the short scholar; 'I should like to hear for myself, at any rate.'

'What sort of ballads do you mean, Sir?' said I to the long scholar.

'Why, those in the Robin Hood Garland, for instance,' said he. 'Songs written for the people, about their heroes, and, I believe, by the people. There's nothing of the sort now.'

'What do you say to "There's a Good Time coming"?' asked the short scholar.

'Well, it's the best of them, I believe,' said the other; 'but you know it was written by Mackay, an LL.D. Besides, it's essentially a town song.'

'It's a tip-top one, at any rate,' said the short scholar; 'I wish I could write such another.'

'What I say, is, that the popular songs now are written by *litterateurs* in London. Is there any life or go in "Woodman spare that Tree," or "The Old Arm-chair"? and they are better than the slip-slop sentimental stuff most in vogue.'

'What a discontented old bird you are!' said the short scholar; 'you're never pleased with any product of this enlightened century.'

'Let the century get a character, then; when it does, we shall get some good staves. I'm not particular; a brave story, or a quaint story, or a funny story, in good rough verse, that's all I ask for. But, where to find one? Here's the Doctor for umpire. I say, Doctor, don't you agree with me, now?'

'Not quite,' said the Doctor, looking up from his cold beef. 'I dare say you wouldn't think them worth much; but there are plenty of ballads sung about which you never hear.'

'What! real modern ballads, written by some of the masses, in this century, for instance? Where did you ever hear one, Doctor? What are they like, now?'

'Well, my work takes me a good deal about in queer places, and at queer times, amongst the country folk, and I hear plenty of them. Will one about Lord Nelson suit you? There's an old patient of mine at the next table who owns a little coal wharf on the canal; he fell into the lock one night, broke his arm, and was nearly drowned, and I attended him. He takes a trip in the barges now and then, which makes him fancy himself half a sailor. I dare say I can set him off, if he hasn't had too much beer.'

So the Doctor walked over to a lower table, and spoke to a grisly-headed old man in a velveteen coat and waistcoat, and a blue birdseye-neckerchief, who seemed pleased, and drew his sleeve across his mouth, and cleared his throat. Then there was a rapping on the table, and the old bargee began in a rumbling bass voice: –

THE DEATH OF LORD NELSON

Come all you gallant seamen as unites a meeting,
 Attend to these lines I be going to relate,
And when you have heard them 'twill move you with pity
 To think how Lord Nelson he met with his fate.
For he was a bold and undaunted commander
 As ever did sail on the ocean so wide;
He made both the French and the Spaniard surrender
 By always a-pouring into them a broadside.

One hundred engagements 'twas he had been into,
 And ne'er in his life was he known to be beat,
Though he'd lost an arm, likewise a right eye, boys,
 No power upon earth ever could him defeat.
His age at his death it was forty and seven;
 And as long as I breathe, his great praises I'll sing;
The whole navigation was given up to him,
 Because he was loyal and true to his king.

Then up steps the doctor in a very great hurry,
 And unto Lord Nelson these words did he say:
'Indeed, then, my Lord, it is I'm very sorry,
 To see you here lying and bleeding this way.'
'No matter, no matter whatever about me,
 My time it is come, I'm almost at the worst;
But here's my gallant seamen a-fighting so boldly,
 Discharge off your duty to all of them first.'

Then with a loud voice, he calls out to his captain,
 'Pray let me, sir, hear how the battle does go,
For I think our great guns do continue to rattle,
 Though death is approaching I firmly do know.'
'The antagonist's ship has gone down to the bottom,
 Eighteen we have captive and brought them on board,
Four more we have blown quite out of the ocean,
 And that is the news I have brought you, my Lord.'

Come all you gallant seamen as unites a meeting,
  Always let Lord Nelson's memory go round,
For it is your duty, when you unites a meeting,
  Because he was loyal and true to the crownd.
And now to conclude and finish these verses,
  'My time it is come; kiss me, Hardy,' he cried.
Now thousands go with you, and ten thousand blessings
  For gallant Lord Nelson in battle who died.

  Mourn, England, mourn, mourn and complain,
  For the loss of Lord Nelson, who died on the main.

The short scholar was in raptures: he shouted in the chorus: he banged the table till he upset and broke his tumbler, which the vigilant landlady from behind the casks duly noted, and scored up to him.

I worked away at my note-book, and managed to get all the song, except one verse between the second and third, which I couldn't catch.

'Bravo, Doctor! Here, waiter, get me another tumbler, and some more gin-punch. What a stunning call. Couldn't the old bird give us another bit of history? It's as good as reading "Southey's Life," and much funnier,' rattled away the short scholar.

'What a quaint old grisly party it is!' said the long scholar; 'I shall stand him a pot of beer.'

'Well, he won't object to that,' said the Doctor, working away at the beef and pickles.

'Here, waiter, take a pot of beer, with my compliments, over to that gentleman,' said the long scholar, pointing to the old bargeman, 'and say how much obliged we are to him for his song.'

So Peter trotted across with the liquor, and the old man telegraphed his acknowledgements.

'By the way, Doctor,' said the short scholar, 'as you seem to know a good deal about these things, can you tell me what "Vicar of Bray" means? I saw two men quarrelling just after the games, and it was all their wives could do to keep them from fighting, and I heard it was because one had called the other "Vicar of Bray."'

'It means "turn-coat" in Berkshire,' answered the Doctor. 'I didn't think they used the name now; but I remember the time when it was the common term of reproach. I dare say you know Bray, gentlemen?'

'I should think so,' said the short scholar; 'pretty village just below Maidenhead. I pulled by it on my way to town last June.'

'Yes, and it's hard on such a pretty village to have had such a bad parson,' said the Doctor.

'I say, Doctor, give us the "Vicar of Bray", now, it will set off some of the singing birds at the other end of the booth; I can see they're getting into prime piping order.'

'Very good, if you like it,' said the Doctor, pushing away his plate, and taking a finishing pull at his pewter, 'only the song is in print, I know, somewhere; so you mustn't think you've found much of a prize, Sir,' added he to me, for my use of pencil and note-book hadn't escaped him.

'No, Sir,' said I; 'but I should like to hear it, of all things.'

So the Doctor, without further preface, began in his jolly clear voice –

THE VICAR OF BRAY

In good King Charles's golden days,
    When loyalty had no harm in't,
A zealous High-Church man I was,
    And so I gained preferment.
To teach my flock I never missed:
    Kings were by God appointed;
And they are damned who dare resist,
    Or touch the Lord's anointed.
        Chorus. – And this is law, I will maintain
                Until my dying day, sir,
                That whatsoever king shall reign,
                I'll be the Vicar of Bray, sir.

When Royal James obtained the throne,
    And Popery grew in fashion,
The Penal Laws I hooted down,
    And read the Declaration;
The Church of Rome I found would fit
    Full well my constitution;
And I had been a Jesuit
    But for the Revolution.
                And this is law, &c.

When William, our deliverer, came
    To heal the nation's grievance,

Then I turned cat-in-pan again,
  And swore to him allegiance;
Old principles I did revoke,
  Set conscience at a distance,
Passive obedience was a joke,
  A jest was non-resistance.
          And this is law, &c.

When glorious Anne became our queen,
  The Church of England's glory,
Another face of things was seen,
  And I became a Tory.
Occasional Conformist case!
  I damned such moderation;
And thought the Church in danger was
  By such prevarication.
          And this is law, &c.

When George in pudding-time came o'er,
  And moderate men looked big, sir,
My principles I changed once more,
  And so became a Whig, sir.
And thus preferment I procurred
  From our Faith's great Defender;
And almost every day abjured
  The Pope and the Pretender.
          For this is law, &c.

The illustrious House of Hanover,
  And Protestant Succession,
By these I lustily will swear
  While they can keep possession;
For in my faith and loyalty
  I never once will falter,
But George my king shall ever be,
  Except the times do alter.
          For this is law, &c.

The shorter scholar was right as to the effect of the Doctor's song. It was hailed with rapturous applause by the lower tables, though you would have said, to look at them, that scarcely a man of the audience except those close round the singer could have appreciated it. People don't always like best what they fully understand; and I don't know which is the greatest mistake, to fancy yourself above your audience, or to try to come down to them. The little stiffness

which the presence of strangers belonging to the broad-cloth classes
had at first created amongst the pastime folk was wearing off, and
several songs were started at once from the distant parts of the
booth, all of which, save one, came to untimely ends in the course of
the first verse or so, leaving the field clear to a ruddy-faced,
smock-frocked man, who, with his eyes cast up to the tent-top,
droned through his nose the following mournful ditty: –

THE BARKSHIRE TRAGEDY

A varmer he lived in the West Countree,
              Hey-down, bow-down,
A varmer he lived in the West Countree,
And he had daughters one, two, and dree.
              And I'll be true to my love,
              If my love'll be true to me.

As thay wur walking by the river's brim,
              Hey-down, bow-down,
As thay wur walking by the river's brim,
The eldest pushed the youngest in.
              And I'll be true, &c.

'Oh sister, oh sister, pray gee me thy hand,
              Hey-down, &c.
And I'll gee thee both house and land.'
              And I'll, &c.

'I'll neither gee thee hand nor glove,
              Hey down, &c.
Unless thou'lt gee me thine own true love.'
              And I'll, &c.

So down she sank and away she swam,
              Hey down, &c.
Until she came to the miller's dam.
              And I'll, &c.

The miller's daughter stood by the door,
              Hey-down, &c.
As fair as any gilly-flow-èr.
              And I'll, &c.

'Oh vather, oh vather, here swims a swan,
              Hey-down, &c.
Very much like a drownded gentlewoman.'
              And I'll, &c.

The miller he got his pole and hook,
                        Hey-down, &c.
And he fished the fair maid out of the brook.
                        And I'll, &c.

'Oh miller, I'll gee thee guineas ten,
                        Hey-down, &c.
If thou'lt fetch me back to my vather again.'
                        And I'll, &c.

The miller he took her guineas ten,
                        Hey-down, &c.
And he pushed the fair maid in again.
                        And I'll, &c.

But the Crowner he cum, and the Justice too,
                        Hey-down, &c.
With a hue and a cry and a hulla-balloo.
                        And I'll, &c.

They hanged the miller beside his own gate,
                        Hey-down, &c.
For drowning the varmer's daughter, Kate.
                        And I'll, &c.

The sister she fled beyond the seas,
                        Hey-down, &c.
And died an old maid among black savagèes.
                        And I'll, &c.

So I've ended my tale of the West Countree.
And they calls it the Barkshire Trage-dèe.
                        And I'll, &c.

'The Barkshire Tragedy, indeed! Now, Doctor, what have you to tell us about this? When did it happen? Who was the lady? Was she drowned in the Thames, the Kennett, or where?'

'Oh, I don't know. All I can say is, she was drowned before my time; for I remember hearing the song when I was a little chap in petticoats. But the story seems a common one. There's a north-country ballad founded on it, I know, but I don't remember the name just now.'

'"The Bonny Mill-dams of Binnorie," is not it?' said the long scholar.

'Aye, that's the name, I think.'

'Well, it's very odd, for we've got the same story, all but the miller, and his daughter as fair as any gilly-flower (why are millers' daughters always pretty, by the way?), on the Welsh marshes,' said the long scholar.

'Then, Sir, I must call on you to sing it. The call is with me at our end of the booth,' said the Doctor. 'And, Peter, bring me a little cold gin-and-water, and a pipe. If I must breathe smoke-poison, I may as well make it myself, at any rate.'

THE DROWNED LADY

Qy. another version of the Barkshire Tragedy?

Oh, it was not a pheasant cock,
   Nor yet a pheasant hen,
But oh it was a lady fair
   Came swimming down the stream.

An ancient harper passing by
   Found this poor lady's body,
To which his pains he did apply
   To make a sweet melòdy.

To cat-gut dried he her inside,
   He drew out her back-bone,
And made thereof a fiddle sweet
   All for to play upon.

And all her hair so long and fair,
   That down her back did flow,
Oh he did lay it up with care,
   To string his fiddle bow.

And what did he with her fingers
   Which were so straight and small?
Oh, he did cut them into pegs
   To screw up his fid-dòll.

Then forth went he, as it might be,
   Upon a summer's day,
And met a goodly company,
   Who asked him in to play.

Then from her bones he drew such tones
  As made their bones to ache,
They sounded so like human groans,
  Their hearts began to quake.

They ordered him in ale to swim,
  For sorrow's mighty dry,
And he to share their wassail fare
  Essayd right willingly.

He laid his fiddle on a shelf
  In that old manor-hall,
It played and sung all by itself,
  And thus sung this fid-dòll: –

'There sits the squire, my worthy sire,
  A-drinking his-self drunk,
And so did he, ah woe is me!
  The day my body sunk.

'There sits my mother, half asleep,
  A-taking of her ease,
Her mind is deep, if one might peep,
  In her preserves and keys.

'There sits my sister, cruel Joan,
  Who last week drownded me;
And there's my love, with heart of stone,
  Sits making love to she.

'There sits the Crowner, Uncle Joe,
  Which comforteth poor me;
He'll hold his Crowner's quest, I know,
  To get his Crowner's fee.'

Now when this fiddle thus had spoke
  It fell upon the floor,
And into little pieces broke,
  No word spoke never more.

'Thank you, Sir,' said the Doctor; 'that's a queer tune though. I don't know that I ever heard one at all like it. But I shouldn't say all that song was old now.'

'Well, I believe you're right. But I can say, as you said of the Barkshire Tragedy, it's all older than my time, for I remember my father singing it just as I've sung it to you as long as I can remember anything.'

'And what did he say of it?'

'Well, he said that five out of the six verses were very old indeed. He had heard them often when he was a child, and always the same words. The rest was all patchwork, he said, by different hands, and he hardly knew which were the old lines, and which new.'

'I say,' remarked the short scholar, 'the Doctor don't seem to be a bad hand at making the smoke-poison.'

The Doctor blew out a long white cloud, and was about to reply, when a brawny young carter, at a distant table, took his pipe from his lips, and, in answer to the urgings of his neighbours, trolled out the following little piece of sentiment: –

CUPID'S GARDEN

As I wur in Cu-bit's gardin
  Not mwoar nor haf an hour,
'T wur ther I zeed two may-dens
  Zittin under Cu-bit's bower,
A-gatherin of sweet jassa-mine,
  The lillỳ and the rose.
These be the fairest flowers
  As in the gardin grows.

I vondly stepped to one o' them,
  These words to her I zays,
'Be you engaged to arra young man,
  Come tell to me, I prays.'
'I beant engaged to narra young man,
  I solemnlỳ declare;
I aims to live a may-den,
  And still the lau-rel wear.'

Zays I, 'My stars and gar-ters!
  This here's a pretty go,
Vor a vine young mayd as never wos
  To sar' all man-kind zo.'
But the t'other young may-den looked sly at me,
  And vrom her zeat she risn,
Zays she, 'Let thee and I go our own way,
  And we'll let she go shis'n.'

'Oh, I say, that beat's all!' said the short scholar, with a shout of laughter. 'I must have the words somehow. Let's see, how did he begin? something about Cubit. What a rum notion to call Cupid, Cubit. What was it, Doctor?'

'You shouldn't laugh, really Sir, at our west-country sentiment,' said the Doctor, with astounding gravity. 'I don't think I can conscientiously help you to the words, when I know you'll only be making fun of them at some wine-party. They are meant for malt drinkers, not for wine drinkers.'

'Fudge, Doctor. Come, now, give us the words, or I shall have to go over and ask the performer for them.'

'I think I can give you them,' said I, looking up from my note-book.

'What a thing it is to write shorthand!' said the Doctor, glancing at my hieroglyphics; 'we don't learn that sort of thing down in these parts.'

'I wonder we haven't had more sentimental songs,' said the long scholar; 'I suppose there are plenty of love stories going about?'

'Oh yes, plenty,' said the Doctor; 'mostly ballads telling how rich young heiresses disdained all good matches, for the sake of a sailor boy with tarry trousers, or a seductive fogger, thereby provoking their cruel match-making parents. For instance: –

'Says the daughter to the mother, "Your art is all in vain,
For Dukes and Lords and Earls alike their riches I disdain;
I'd rather live a humble life, and my time I would employ
Increasing nature's prospects, with my bonny labouring boy".'

'What on earth can "increasing nature's prospects" mean?' asked the long scholar.

'How can I tell?' said the Doctor, laughing; 'I don't pretend to construe; I only give you the words. But you must allow the moral to be good. It runs: –

'Success to every labouring boy that ploughs and hoes the ground,
For when his work is over, his home he will enjoy;
So happy is the girl that gets a bonny labouring boy.'

'Let's see,' said the short scholar, 'we've had specimens of patriotic, legendary, and sentimental ditties; but how about drinking songs? All tuneful nations, since the world began, have sung the praises of good liquor.'

'I don't know that we have many drinking songs,' said the Doctor; 'I suppose it takes wine, or spirits at any rate, to make a man write such stuff as "the glasses sparkle," or "a bumper of Burgundy." The bucolic muse only gets smallish beer. But we must see what we can do for you.' So the Doctor beckoned to Peter, and sent him off to the lower tables with a pot of beer, the speedy result of which mission was the following song: –

TOVEY'S TAP – AIR, *'Derry down.'*

Owld Tovey once brewed a barrel o' beer,
For he wur a man as lovèd good cheer,
And zays he, 'I'll jest ax a veaw o' my vriends
To come and try how the likker spends.'*
Derry down, &c.

There's long Tom Ockle, he shall be one,
And little Jack Smith, who's as round as a tun,
And owld Gaarge Mabbott, who's allus a-dry,
I'll warn'd thay'll make good company.
Derry down, &c.

The barrell wur tapped, and the beer runned well,
How much they vour drenked I never heard tell;
But zome how or other they one and all
Did zwear as how the drenk wur small.
Derry down, &c.

Owld Tovey at this did look main scrow;†
Zays he, 'My vriends, I'd hev'ee to kneow
That my beer has made 'ee as drunk as pegs,
And not one o' you dree can kip on his legs.'
Derry down, &c.

They left the house, and the path they tuk,
Athert the meadow as leads to the bruk;
And you plainly med zee as every man
Had a pair o' crooked stockings an.
Derry down, &c.

Zays Mabbott to Ockle, 'Owld Tovey wur zurly;'
Zays Ockle to Mabbott, 'I'm uncommon purly; ‡

Be mindful, I say, vor yer missuses' zakes,
Which o' them two narrer bridges you takes.'
                                    Derry down, &c.

'The bruk is main deep,' Gaarge Mabbott then zaid,
As he looked at the water, and scratted his yead;
And I owns I should 'mazinly like for to know
Auver which o' thay bridges you aims vor to go.'
                                    Derry down, &c.

'Tis a akkerdish place to crass in the night,
And to stand here till marnin' wouldn't be right;
'T'aint a mossell o' use to bide stabbleing** here,
Zo let's go back and vinish the barrel o' beer.'
                                    Derry down, &c.

*   'Spend' – to consume.
†   'Scrow' – angry.
‡   'Purly' – purblind.
** 'Stabble' – to tread dirt about.

'A good cast, Doctor;' said the long scholar; 'but you've raised the wrong fish. That isn't what my friend here meant by a drinking song. He expects a bucolic rendering of one of Moore's songs, and you serve him out a queer pot-house tale. Is there no enthusiasm for good drink amongst you?'

'I wish there were less,' said the Doctor, with a sigh; 'at any rate, less consumption of bad drink. Tippling is our great curse, as it is that of all England; but there's less of it than there used to be. But for a drinking song such as you mean, I'm at fault. The nearest approach to it that I know of is a song of which I only remember two lines. They run –

'Sartinly the sixpenny's the very best I've see'd yet,
I do not like the fourpenny, nor yet the intermediate.

But even here you see, though the poet was meditating on drink, it was in a practical rather than an enthusiastic spirit.'

Just then, a stout old yeoman entered the booth, dressed in a broad straight-cut brown coat with metal buttons, drab breeches, and mahogany tops; and, marching up to the bar, ordered a glass of brandy and water; while his drink was being prepared, he stood with his back to our table, talking to the landlord.

'We're in luck,' said the Doctor in a low voice, pointing to the new-comer with the end of his pipe; 'if he stays, we shall have the best old song in all the west country, sung as it should be.'

'Who is he?' asked the short scholar.

'An old Gloucestershire farmer from Sutherup way, famous for his breed of sheep. He must be near seventy, and has twelve miles to ride home tonight, and won't think so much of it as you or I would.'

'He looks a tough old blade.'

'You may say that. But he isn't the man he was, for he has lived pretty hard. He used to be a famous wrestler; and one day, many years ago, an Ilsley dealer came down to buy his flock of two-year olds. They drank six bottles of port over the deal, and got it all straight out except the odd sheep, but they couldn't make out, cipher it how they would, who the odd sheep belonged to; so they agreed to wrestle for the odd sheep in the farmer's kitchen, and somehow both of them got hurt, and the old boy has never gone quite right since.'

'What an old sponge! six bottles of port between two of them! no wonder they couldn't do their sum.'

'Ah, we mustn't judge of the men of his times by our rules,' said the Doctor: 'it was part of a yeoman's creed in those days to send his friends off drunk, and to be carried to bed himself by his fogger and carter, or else to sleep under his kitchen-table. They lived hard enough, and misused a deal of good liquor meant to strengthen man's heart, following the example of their betters; but they had their good points. That old man, now, is the best master in all his neighbourhood; and he and the parson keep up the wages in the winter, and never let a man go to the house who will work.'

The old farmer turned round, glass in hand, and came and sat down at the table. 'Your sarvant, gen'l'men,' said he, taking off his broad-brimmed beaver. 'Why, Doctor,' he went on, recognising our friend, and holding out his great bony hand, 'be main glad to zee 'ee.'

'Thank you, farmer,' said the Doctor, returning the grip: 'we haven't met this long while; I'm glad to see you wearing so well.'

'Yes, I be pretty-feteish, thank God,' said the farmer. 'Your health, sir, and gen'l'men.'

After a little judicious talk on the day's sport, the Doctor suddenly began, 'Now, farmer, you must do us a favour, and give us your famous old Gloucestershire song. I've been telling all our friends here about it, and they're keen to hear it.'

''Spose you means Gaarge Ridler?' said the farmer.

'Of course,' said the Doctor.

'Well, I don't know as I've zung these score o' months,' said the farmer, 'but hows'mever, if you wants it, here goes.' So the farmer finished his brandy and water, cleared his throat, balanced himself on the hind legs of his chair, cast up his eyes and began –

> Thaay stwuns, thaay stwuns, thaay stwuns, thaay stwuns,
> Thaay stwuns, thaay stwuns, thaay stwuns, thaay stwuns.

'What's he saying – what language?' whispered the tall scholar.

'Mad old party,' mumbled the short scholar.

'Hush,' whispered the Doctor; 'that's the orthodox way to begin; don't put him out.'

I couldn't tell what in the world to write, but the farmer went on with growing emphasis –

> Thaay stwuns, thaay stwuns, thaay stwuns, thaay stwuns,
> Thay stwuns, thaay stwuns, *thaay stwuns,* THAAY S, T, W, U, N, S.

There was a moment's pause, during which the Doctor had much difficulty in keeping order; then the farmer got fairly under weigh, and went on –

> They stwuns that built Gaarge Ridler's oven,
>   Oh, thaay cum vrom the Blakeney Quaar,
> And Gaarge he wur a jolly owld man,
>   And his yead did graw above his yare.
>
> One thing in Gaarge Ridler I must commend,
>   And I hold it vor a notable thing:
> He made his braags avoore he died,
>   As wi' any dree brothers his zons zhou'd zing.
>
> Ther' wur Dick the treble, and Jack the mean,
>   Let every mon zing in his auwn pleace,
> And Gaarge he wur the elder brother,
>   And there-voore he would zing the base.

Droo' aal the world, owld Gaarge would bwoast,
　Commend me to merry owld England mwoast,
While vools gwoes scamblin' vur and nigh,
　We bides at whoam, my dog and I.

Ov their furrin tongues let travellers brag,
　Wi' their vifteen neames vor a puddin' bag,
Two tongues I knows ne'er towld a lie,
　And their wearers be my dog and I.

My dog has got his maaster's nose,
　To smell a knave droo' silken hose;
But when good company I spy,
　'Welcome,' quoth my dog and I.

When I hev dree sixpences under my thumb,
　Oh then I be welcome wherever I cum;
But when I hev none, O then I pass by;
　'Tis poverty pearts good company.

When I gwoes dead, as it may hap,
　My grave shall be under the good yeal-tap,
Wi' vaulded earmes ther' wool I lie,
　Cheek by jowl, my dog and I.

Just as the farmer was finishing the song, Master George with Joe and one or two more behind him, came in. He took up the last verse, and rolled it out as he came up towards our table, and a lot of the rest joined in with him; even the over-worked Peter, I could see stopping for a moment to shout that he would be buried under the tap; I dare say he meant it, only I think he would like it to be always running.

Master George knew most of the people, and made us all merrier even than we were before; and in the next half-hour or so, for which time we stayed in the booth, I should think there must have been a dozen more songs sung. However, I shall only give the one which seemed to be the greatest favourite, for I find that this chapter is running very long. This song was sung by a queer little man, with a twisted face, and a lurcher dog between his knees, who I believe was an earth stopper. He called it

BUTTERMILK JACK

Ther wur an owld 'oman as had but one son,
And they lived together as you med zee;
And they'd nought but an owld hen as wanted to sett,
Yet somehow a landlord he fain would be.

'Oh, I've been and begged me some buttermilk, mother,
Off of an owld 'oman as has girt store;
And I shall well rewarded be,
Vor she's g'in me haf a gallon or mwore.

'Oh mother, my buttermilk I will sell,
And all for penny as you med zee;
And with my penny then I will buy eggs,
Vor I shall have seven for my pennèy.

'Oh mother, I'll set them all under our hen,
And seven cock chickens might chance for to be;
But seven cock chickens or seven cap hens,
There'll be seven half-crownds for me.

'Oh, I'll go carry them to market, mother,
And nothing but vine volk shall I zee;
And with my money then I will buy land,
Zo as a landlord I med be.'

'Oh my dear zon, wilt thee know me,
When thee hast gotten great store of wealth?'
'Oh, my dear mother, how shall I know thee,
When I shall hardly know my own self?'

With that the owld 'oman she flew in a passion,
And dashed her son Jack up agin the wall,
And his head caught the shelf where the buttermilk stood,
So down came the buttermilk, pitcher and all.

Zo aal you as has got an old hen for to sett,
Both by night and by day mind you has her well watched,
Let you should be like unto Buttermilk Jack,
To reckon your chickens before they are hatched.

'Well, I must be moving,' said the Doctor at last, looking at his watch; 'how do you get home, Mr Hurst?'

'Bless us! near nine o'clock,' said Joe, following the Doctor's example; 'oh, I ride myself, and my friend here talks of going behind.'

'Better not ride double, the night's dark,' said the Doctor, hoisting on his over-coat with Peter's help. 'If he likes to take his luck in my gig, I can put him down at your gate. What do you say, Sir?'

I thankfully accepted; for I didn't at all like the notion of riding behind Joe on the chestnut, and I can't think how I could ever have been such a foool as to say I would do it. The Doctor had two bright lamps to his gig, which gave us glimpses of the closed booths and camping places of the people who were going to stay on the hill all night, as we drove out of the Castle. I suggested that it must be very bad for the people sleeping out up there.

'For their health?' said he, 'not a bit of it, on a fine night like this – do 'em good: I wish they always slept so healthily.'

'I didn't quite mean that, Sir!'

'Oh, for their morals? Well, I don't know that there's much harm done. I'm sorry to say they're used to crowding – and, after all, very few but the owners of the booths, and the regular tramps, stay up here. Didn't you see how quiet everything was?'

I said I had noticed this; and then he began asking me about the sports, for he had only got on to the hill late in the afternoon; and when we came to the wrestling and backsword play, I asked him whether he thought they did any harm.

'No,' said he, 'there are very few serious accidents – in fact none – now that drink is not allowed on the stage. There used to be some very brutal play in out-of-the-way places, where the revels were got up by publicans. But that is all over, at least about this part of the country.'

'Then you wouldn't stop them, Sir?'

'Stop them! not I – I would encourage them, and make the parish clerk and constable perpetual umpires.' And then he went on to say how he should like to see the young fellows in every parish drilled in a company, and taught all sorts of manly exercises, and shooting especially; so that they would make good light troops at a day's notice, in case of invasion. But he was afraid the great game preserves would never allow this. And in the middle of his talk, which seemed very sensible, we came to Joe's gate, and I got down, and wished him good night.

I found the family gone to bed, and only Joe and the Parson in the kitchen, and there, over a last pipe, we chatted about the sports.

At last the Parson turned to me and said, 'You saw a good deal of the play on the stage; now, would you stop it if you could?'

I thought a minute over what I had seen and what the Doctor had said.

'No, Sir,' said I, 'I can't say that I would.'

'That's candid,' said he. 'And now I'll make an admission. There's a good deal of the play that wants very close watching. The umpires should be resolute quick men, and stand no nonsense. I saw one or two bouts today that should have been stopped.'

'You see,' said Joe, taking his pipe out of his mouth, 'there allus must be.'

'We don't admit your evidence, Joseph,' interrupted the Parson, 'you are a prejudiced witness.'

'But you haven't changed your mind, Sir,' said I.

'No,' said he, 'I should be sorry to hear that these sports had died out, but I should like to hear that people took an interest in them who could manage the men thoroughly.'

'The Doctor,' said I, 'as we drove home, said he would have the parish clerk and constable for perpetual umpires.'

'They wouldn't be so good as the parson or the squire,' said he; 'if I were rector of one of the parishes where they are still kept up, I would give prizes for them, but I would always be umpire myself.'

'I wish to goodness you was then,' said Joe, as we lighted our candles.

'You remember, Sir,' said I, 'that you promised to write a sermon about the pastime.'

'What! *after* the fair?' said he.

'''Twill do just as well,' said Joe, 'I should mortally like to hear it.'

'Well, it might keep you awake perhaps. He has an hereditary weakness for slumber in church, you must know,' said the Parson, turning to me; 'when we wanted to alter the sittings in the church six or seven years ago, his father stood out for his old high box so sturdily, that I took some pains to argue with him, and to find out what it was which made it so dear to him. I found out at last that it was a snug corner, which just fitted his shoulders, where nobody could see him, and where, as soon as the text was given out, in his own words, "I just watches my missus wipe her spectacles, and fix herself to listen, and then I vaulds my arms and thenks o' nothin".'

I looked at Joe to see how he would take it, but he only chuckled and said, 'Well, 'tis the parson's business to keep us awake. But a sermon on our sports, just showing folk about the rights on it, is just what I should amazingly like to have by me.'

The Parson looked at Joe for a moment very curiously, and then said, 'Very well, I will write you one. Good night.'

And so we went off to bed.

CHAPTER VIII

MISS Lucy couldn't be spared to go up to the hill on the second day of the pastime, for there was some great operation going on in the cheese room, which she had to overlook. So Mr Warton drove me up in the four-wheel. I was very anxious to find out, if I could, whether there was anything more between him and Miss Lucy than friendship, but it wasn't at all an easy matter. First I began speaking of the young gentleman who had taken my place in the four-wheel; for I thought that would be a touchstone, and that if he were like me he would be glad to get a chance of abusing this Jack. But he only called him a forward boy, and said he was a cousin of the Hursts, who lived in the next parish. Then I spoke of Miss Lucy herself, and he was quite ready to talk about her as much as I liked, and seemed never tired of praising her. She was a thoroughly good specimen of an English yeoman's daughter; perfectly natural, and therefore perfectly well bred: not above making good puddings and preserves, and proud of the name her brother's cheeses had won in the market, yet not negligent of other matters, such as the schools, and her garden: never going into follies of dress in imitation of weak women who ought to set better examples, yet having a proper appreciation of her own good looks, and a thorough knowledge of the colours and shapes which suited her best: not particularly clever or well read, but with an open mind and a sound judgment – and so he went on; and the longer he went on the more I was puzzled, and my belief is, that on this subject the Parson got much more out of me than I out of him, on that morning's drive.

We had a very pleasant day on the hill, but as the sports were all the same as those of the day before (with the exception of jumping in sacks, which was substituted for climbing the pole, and was very good fun), I shall not give any further account of them; especially as the gentlemen who are going to publish my story seem to think already that I am rather too long-winded.

We got down home in capital time for tea, and Joe followed very soon afterwards, in the highest spirits; for, as he said, everything had gone off so well, and everybody was pleased and satisfied; so we were all very merry, and had another charming evening. I couldn't tell what had come to me when I got up stairs alone by myself, for I seemed as if a new life were growing up in me, and I were getting all of a sudden into a much bigger world, full of all sorts of work and pleasure, which I had never dreamt of, and of people whom I could get to love and honour, though I might never see or speak to them.

I had been bred up from a child never to look beyond my own narrow sphere. To get on in it was the purpose of my life, and I had drilled myself into despising everything which did not, as I thought, help towards this end. Near relations I had none. I was really fond of my two friends, but I don't think I should ever have got to be friends with them if we hadn't been in the same office; and I used often to be half provoked with them, and to think myself a very wise fellow, because out of office-hours they would read poetry and novels instead of fagging at shorthand or accounts, as I did, and spent all their salaries instead of saving. Except those two, I knew nobody; and though I belonged to a debating society, it wasn't that I cared for the members, or what they talked about, but that I thought it might be useful to me to talk fluently if I got on in business. Sometimes, and especially in my yearly holidays, I had felt as if I wanted something else, and that my way of life was after all rather a one-eyed sort of business; but I set all such misgivings down as delusions, and had never allowed them long to trouble me. In short I begin to suspect that I must have been getting to be a very narrow, bigoted, disagreeable sort of fellow, and it was high time that I should find my way to Elm Close, or some such place, to have my eyes opened a little, and discover that a man may work just as steadily and honestly – aye, much more steadily and honestly – at his own business, without shutting up his brains and his heart against everything else that is going on in the world around him. However, I can't be too thankful that my teaching came to me in the way it did, for I might have had to learn my lesson in a very different school from Elm Close Farm.

There certainly never was such a pleasant school. For the next two or three days after 'the Scouring,' Mr Warton was my chief companion. Joe and Miss Lucy both had their work to attend to after breakfast, and so the Parson and I were left a good deal together; and we used to start off to see some of the old men whom he had promised to show me, who could tell me about the old pastimes. I never liked anything so much as these walks – not even the walks I afterwards used to have alone with Miss Lucy, for they were too exciting, and half the time I was in such a fret that I couldn't thoroughly enjoy them. But there was no drawback in these walks with the Parson. He was full of fun, and of all sorts of knowledge; and he liked talking, and I think rather took a fancy to me, and was pleased to see how I worked at collecting all the information I could about the White Horse, for he took a great deal of pains to help me.

One morning though I remember he got me into a regular puzzle about King Alfred, for I had been reading over my notes of the old gentleman's story, and couldn't make it agree with the tales which I had read about Alfred's hiding away in the cowherd's hut, and burning the cakes. So I asked Mr Warton about it.

'I think,' said he, 'you will find that Alfred was in the cowherd's cottage in the year 878, after the battle at Chippenham.'

'But, Sir,' said I, 'according to the old gentleman's story, Ashdown was Alfred's greatest victory; and Ashdown was fought in 871. Now it seems very odd that he should have to run away and skulk about in such places after that.'

'Well,' said he, 'I'm not well enough up in the history to explain it to you, but I'm pretty sure you'll find I'm right about the dates – why shouldn't you write and ask the old gentleman?'

So, I did, and I kept a copy of my letter; but I don't think I need print that, because his answer will be quite enough without it. Here it is: –

> 22nd September, 1857.
>
> My Dear Sir, – I am favoured with yours of the 20th ult., which came safely to hand this morning. Our post is somewhat behind the times, and I know of hardly any town or village from which a letter can arrive at this place under two days. I do not myself complain of this state of things.
>
> With regard to the subject of your letter, I have to tell you that your friend the clergyman is right in his dates. It was in the year 878 that Alfred was deserted by his nobles and people after the battle of Chippenham, which was a drawn battle. Then he fled to the Island of Athelney, in Somersetshire, and the incident to which you allude took place, but you have not got the verses correctly: they run,
>
> 'Casn't mind the ke-aks mun, and doosn't zee 'em burn?
> I'ze warn thee'lt yeat 'em vast enough, zo zoon az 'tiz thy turn.'

But you are not to believe from this, that the Danish army ever got a hold on the kingdom of Wessex. I think that the following passage from Asser's 'Life of Alfred' will explain a good deal to you. Referring to his sojourn in Athelney, Asser says:

'We may believe that this misfortune was brought upon the aforesaid king, because in the beginning of his reign, when he was a youth, and influenced by youthful feelings, he would not listen to the petitions which his subjects made to him for help in their necessities; but he drove them from him and paid no heed to their requests. This particular gave much pain to the holy man, St Neot, who was his kinsman; and often foretold to him in the spirit of prophecy that he would suffer great adversity on this account: but Alfred neither attended to the reproof of the man of God, nor listened to his true prophecy – wherefore seeing that a man's sins must be corrected either in this world or the next, the true and rightous Judge willed that his sin should not go unpunished in this world, to the end that he might spare him in the world to come. From this cause, therefore, Alfred often fell into such great misery, that sometimes none of his subjects knew where he was, or what had become of him.'

And Alfred learned his lesson well in the next few years, for you will find that in the year 886 AD, 'which was the thirty-eighth year since his birth, King Alfred, after the burning of cities and slaying of the people, honourably rebuilt the city of London and made it again habitable, and gave it into the custody of his son-in-law, Æthelred, Earl of Mercia: to which King Alfred, all the Angles and Saxons, who before had been dispersed everywhere, or were in captivity with the pagans, voluntarily turned and submitted themselves to his rule!'

You see they had turned from his rule many of them because it was an unjust one in those early years of his reign. But they were never subdued by the Danes, – so that my statement which you quote, 'that the battle of Ashdown saved England from one hundred years of Paganism,' is not shaken.

I have directed my London bookseller to leave a copy of Asser's 'Life of Alfred the Great,' for you, at Somerset House, directed to the care of my friend, the secretary of the Antiquaries' Society; you will find it to be well worth a careful perusal. I shall be always glad to hear from you upon the subjects on which we have conversed, and heartily desiring that the veneration for all that is old may grow upon you, and that God may have you in his good keeping, I am, faithfully yours,

'————.'

But to return to my subject, from which I have been wandering for the pleasure of putting in the old gentleman's letter. The Parson in our walks set me thinking about fifty subjects which I never cared about before, because I could see that he was himself deeply interested in them, and really believed whatever he said to me. We used to get home by about twelve o'clock, and then I would go away by myself, and think over what we had been talking about till dinner. And, after dinner, Miss Lucy, and sometimes Joe, would come out and walk with us till tea. Sometimes we went to the village school, and I sat at the door and heard them teaching; and as long as Mr Warton was with us it was all right, but afterwards, when he had gone, I could see that the schoolmistress, a young woman of about thirty, sallow-faced and rather prudish, used to look at me as if I had no business there.

When he left, Mr Warton gave me a kind invitation to go and see him in town, and added he had no doubt I should come, for he could see I should soon want some such work as he could give me to do.

After he was gone I tumbled fairly head over heels into the net in which I suppose every man 'as is a man' (as old Seeley would say) gets enmeshed once in his life. I found it was no use to struggle any longer, and gave myself up to the stream, with all sails set. Now there is no easier thing than going down stream somehow, when wind and tide are with you; but to steer so as to make the most of wind and tide isn't so easy – at least I didn't find it so.

For as often as not, I think, I did the wrong thing, and provoked, instead of pleasing her. I used to get up every morning before six, to be ready to wish her good morning as she went out to the dairy; but I don't think she half liked it, for she was generally in a very old gown tucked through her pocket holes, and pattens. Then after breakfast I used to hanker round the kitchen, or still-room, or wherever she might happen to be, like a Harry-long-legs round a candle. And again in the afternoon I never could keep away, but was at her side in the garden, or on her walks; in fact, to get rid of me, she had fairly to go up to her room.

But I couldn't help myself; I felt that, come what might, I must be near her while I could; and on the whole, I think she was pleased, and didn't at all dislike seeing me reduced to this pitiful state.

When I was involuntarily out of her sight, I used to have a sort of craving for poetry, and often wished that I had spent a little more time over such matters. I got Joe to lend me the key of the cupboard where he kept his library, hoping to find something to suit me there. But, besides a few old folios of divinity and travel, and some cookery books, and the Farmer's Magazine, there was nothing but Watts's Hymns and Pollock's Course of Time, which I didn't find of any use to me.

Joe used to wonder at me at first, when I refused his offers of a day's coursing, or a ride with him to Farringdon or Didcot markets;

but he soon got used to it, and put it down to my cockney bringing up, and congratulated himself that, at any rate, I was pretty good company over a pipe in the kitchen.

The autumn days sped away all too quickly, but I made the most of them as they passed, and over and over again I wondered whether there were any but kind and hospitable and amusing people in the Vale, for the longer I stayed there, the more I was astonished at the kind courtesy of everybody I came across, from the highest to the lowest, and I suppose everybody else would find it the same as I did.

It seemed as if I were destined to leave Elm Close without a single unkind thought of anybody I had seen while there, for even Jack made his peace with me. Only two days before my departure, Miss Lucy gave out at breakfast that she was going to walk over to see her uncle, and wanted to know if her mother or Joe had any message. No, they hadn't. But of course I managed to accompany her.

When we came to her uncle's farm, he was out, and in five minutes Miss Lucy was away with her dear friend and cousin, one of the girls I had seen at the pastime, and I was left to the tender mercies of Jack. However, Jack at his own house, with no women by to encourage him to make a fool of himself, was a very decent fellow. He walked me about the homestead, and chatted away about the pastime, and the accomplishments of his terrier dog, whom he had got from the kennel of the Berkshire hounds, and whose father used to run with them regularly. Then be began to inquire about me in a patronising way; how I came to know Joe, what I was, and where I lived. And when he had satisfied his curiosity about me, he took to talking about his cousins. Joe, I soon found out, was his hero; and he looked forward to the time when he should be able to breed a good horse, like Joe's chestnut, and to go about to all the markets and carry his head as high as any one, as Joe could, as the height of human happiness. As to cousin Lu, if he were looking out for anything of the sort, there was no girl within twenty miles that he knew of to whom she couldn't give a stone over any country. But she wasn't likely to marry any of the young men about; she was too full of fun, and laughed at them too much. 'I shouldn't be a bit surprised now, if she was to take to some town chap like you, after all's said and done,' said Jack, in conclusion, as we returned to the house.

My last day at Elm Close came swiftly and surely, and the sun rose, and went pitilessly up into the heavens, and sank down behind

White Horse Hill, and the clocks went on striking one after another, just as if it had been any other day. What a number of things I had in my head that morning to say to all of them, and above all to her; but one thing or another interfered, and I had said not one quarter of them, and these not in the way I had intended, before it was dark, and tea on the table. But I did go all round the farm and the village, and took a last look at every field and nook and corner where I had been so happy.

The old lady was unusually talkative at tea, and for some time afterwards. The fact that I was not going to leave the house till after midnight, and was to be at business, in London, at nine o'clock the next morning, now that she had realised it, excited her very much, and waked up all sorts of recollections of her own travels; particularly how, when she was a child, she had been a whole day getting to Reading by the stage, and how, even after her marriage, she and father had had to sleep at Windsor, on the occasion of their one visit to London. I was watching Miss Lucy at her work all the time, and thought she seemed a little absent and sorrowful, and when our eyes met every now and then, she looked away directly. We hardly said a word, and left Joe to keep up the talk with the old lady.

Before long she got tired and went off to bed, and then, I thought, if something would only call Joe out – but nothing happened, and so we sat on talking commonplaces, till prayer time; which, however, Joe did consent to put off this evening, because it was my last, till past ten o'clock. The three servants came in, and knelt down as usual; and I, in a place where I could see her, and watch every turn of her figure, and hear every breath she drew. I own I didn't listen to a word that Joe read – I couldn't – and I don't believe any poor fellow in my state will ever be hardly judged, whatever square-toed people may say, for not forcing himself to attend when he hasn't the power to do it. I only know that, though I couldn't listen to the prayers, I could and did thank God for having brought me down there, and allowed me to see her and know her; and prayed, as heartily as was in me to pray, that I might never do anything which might make me unworthy of one so bright, and pure, and good as she.

And too soon Joe shut the book, and got up, and the servants went out, and Joe dived off into the recess; and she lighted her candle and came up to me, holding out her hand, but without saying anything, or looking up in my face.

I took the hand which she held out to me in both mine, and somehow, when I thought it might be for the last time, I couldn't let it go. So I stood holding it, my heart beating so that I couldn't speak, and feeling very uncomfortable about the throat. She didn't take it away, and presently I got my voice again.

'Good bye, Miss Lucy,' said I. 'and God bless you. I can't tell you what my holiday at Elm Close has been to me – and I can't find words to thank you. I'm a poor lonely fellow, with nobody belonging to me, and leading a slave of a life in the midst of the great crowd, with all sorts of temptations to go wrong. You'll let me think of you, and Elm Close, and it will be like a little bright window with the sun shining through into our musty clerks' room. I feel it will help to keep me straight for many a long day. You'll let me think of you now, won't you?' said I, pressing the little hand which I held in mine.

'Why, you see I can't help it if I would,' said she, looking up with a merry light in her eyes; but she went on directly, 'but, indeed, I'm sure we shall think of you quite as often as you will of us. Joe used to talk to often about you that I felt quite like an old friend before we met, and now you've been here we shall feel so dull without you.'

'Now, you two! don't stand talking there all night,' said Joe, coming out of the recess, where he had been rummaging out the pipes and a black bottle; 'come, come, kiss and part.'

I felt the blood rush up to my face, when Joe said that, but I opened my hands with a jerk, and let her's go, I hardly knew why. If I hadn't been so fond that I was afraid of her, I should have taken Joe at his word. But I'm glad I didn't; I'm sure I was right, for I stole a look at her, and saw that she looked vexed, and flushed up to her bright brown hair. Next moment she held out her hand again, and shook mine heartily, and said, without looking up, 'Good-bye, you must come again soon,' and then hurried out of the room, and took away all the light with her. Heigh-ho! when shall I see the light again?

Well, as I followed Joe into the kitchen, what between the sinking I felt at having to leave, and the doubt whether I hadn't made a fool of myself at the last with Miss Lucy, I felt half mad, and the first thing I made up my mind to was to have a good quarrel with Joe.

So when he sat down on one side of the fire, and began lighting his pipe, I kept standing looking at him, and thinking how I should begin.

'There's your pipe, Dick,' said he, puffing away, 'on the settle – why don't you sit down and light up?'

'I shan't smoke with you tonight, Joe,' said I, 'you ought to be ashamed of yourself!'

'Ashamed o' myself,' shouted Joe, staring up at me till I could hardly keep from laughing, angry as I was; 'what, in the name o' goodness, have I done to be ashamed of?'

''Tisn't what you've done, but what you've said.'

'Said! what in the world have I said? Precious little I know, for you always get all the talk to yourself.'

'Why, what you said just now to me and Miss Lucy,' said I.

'To you and Lu?' said he, looking puzzled; and then off he went into one of his great laughs. 'Oh, I take – well, that's too much! To be blown up by *you* for it! Why, if any one is to scold, I should say it's Lu.'

'Do you think I like to be made the means of giving your sister pain?' said I.

'There now, don't be a fool, Dick – sit down like a good fellow and light your pipe. What I said don't mean anything down in these parts. Well, I'm very sorry. She'll never think twice about it, bless you. And besides, you know, there can't be any harm done, for you didn't take my advice.'

Well, I began to get cool, and to think I might do something better than quarrel with Joe the last night; so I took my pipe, and filled it, and sat down opposite him, and he began to mix two glasses of grog, twisting his face about all the time to keep himself from laughing.

'Here's your health, old fellow,' said he, when he had done, 'and, mind you, we shall always be glad to see you here when you can come; though I'm afraid the place must be terrible dull for a Londoner.'

'It's the best place I've ever been in,' said I, with a sigh.

This pleased Joe; and he went off about what he would find me to do if I could come down in the winter or the spring; but I didn't listen much, for I was making up my mind to speak to him about his sister, and I was afraid how he might take it.

Presently he stopped for a moment, and I thought, 'now or never,' and began.

'I want to ask you, Joe, is your sister engaged to any one?'

'Not she,' said Joe, looking up rather surprised; 'why, she's only eighteen come Lady-day!'

'What do you think of Mr Warton?' said I.

'Our Parson!' laughed Joe; 'that is a good 'un. Why he has got a sweetheart of his own. Let alone that he'd know better than to court a farmer's daughter.'

'Are you sure?' said I; 'your sister isn't like most girls, I can tell you.'

'Yes, I tell you,' said Joe, 'he's no more in love with our Lu than you are.'

'Then I'm over head and ears in love with her, and that's all about it,' said I, and I looked straight across at him, though it wasn't an easy thing to do. But I felt I was in for it, and I should be much better for having it over.

Joe gave a start, and a long whistle; and then a puff or two at his pipe, staring at me right in the eyes till I felt my head swimming. But I wasn't going to look down just then; if he had looked me right through he couldn't have found anything I was ashamed of, so far as his sister was concerned, and I felt he had a right to look as hard as he pleased, and that I was bound not to shirk it.

Presently he got up, and took a turn or two up and down the kitchen. Then he stopped –

'Spoke to her, yet?' said he.

'No,' said I, 'I haven't.'

'Come, give us your hand, Dick,' said he, holding out his, and looking quite bright again; 'I knew you would be all on the square, let be what might.'

'Well, I won't deceive you, Joe,' said I, 'I don't deserve any credit for that.'

'How not?' said he.

'Why, I meant to have spoken to her half-a-dozen times, only one little thing or another stopped it. But I'm very glad of it, for I think you ought to know it first.'

'Well, well,' said he, coming and sitting down again, and staring into the fire, 'it's a precious bad job. Let's think a bit how we be to tackle it.'

'I know,' said I, drawing up a bit – for I didn't feel flattered at this speech – 'that I'm not in the same position you are in, and that you've a right to look for a much richer man than I am for your sister, but –'

'Oh, bother that,' said Joe, beginning to smoke again, and still staring into the fire; 'I wasn't thinking of that. 'Twill be just as bad

for we, let who will take her. Here's mother getting a'most blind, and
'mazing forgetful-like about everything. Who's to read to her her
chapter, or to find her spectacles? and what in the world's to become
of the keys? I be no use to mother by myself, you see,' said Joe, 'and
I couldn't abide to see the old lady put about at her time of life; let
alone how the pickling and preserving is to go on.'

I was very pleased and surprised to see him taking it so coolly, and
particularly that he seemed not to be objecting to me, but only to
losing his sister at all.

'Then there's my dairy,' said he; 'that cow Daisy, as gives the
richest milk in all the Vale, nobody could ever get her to stand quiet
till Lucy took to her; she'll kick down a matter o' six pail o' milk a
week, I'll warrant. And the poultry, too; there's that drattl'd old
galleeny 'll be learning the Spanish hens to lay astray up in the brake,
as soon as ever Lu goes, and then the fox 'll have 'em all. To think of
the trouble I took to get that breed, and not a mossel o' use at last!'

'Well, but Joe,' said I, 'one would think we were going to be
married tomorrow, to hear you talk.'

'Well, you want to be married, don't you?' said he, looking up.

'Yes, but not directly,' said I; 'you see, I should like to have a tidy
place got all ready before I should think –'

'Why, she mayn't be agreeable after all,' interrupted Joe, as if a
new light had suddenly struck him; and then he had a good laugh at
the thought, in which I didn't join.

'Then, Joe,' said I, 'I think you don't seem to mind my being a
cockney, and not a rich man?'

'I'd sooner have had a chap that knows a horse from a hand-spike,
and something about four-course,' said he, 'so I won't tell a lie about
it, Dick. Put that out of the way, and I'd as lief call you brother-in-
law as any man. But you ain't in any hurry you said just now?'

'Well, no,' said I; 'but of course I should like to write to your sister
directly and tell her, and I hope you won't object to that, and won't
hinder me if you can't help me.'

'Don't have any of that writing,' said Joe, ''pend upon it a
good-bred girl like Lu wouldn't stand it.'

'That's all very well,' said I, 'but I'm going away tonight, you
know, and if I don't write how's she ever to know anything about it?'

'Look here,' said Joe; 'will you promise, Dick, to give me and
mother a year to turn round in from next Christmas – that is,

supposing Lu don't say no?'

'Yes, certainly,' said I. 'Christmas year is the earliest time I could hope to be ready by.'

'Then I'll tell you what,' said he; 'don't you go writing to her at all, and I'll bring her up with me for Christmas cattle show, and you can get us lodgings, and show us some of the sights. You can have it all out with her before we come home, and I shall be by to see all fair.'

'No, no, Joe, I couldn't say a word with you by.'

'I didn't mean that I was to be in the room, you know, only if anything goes wrong – you understand,' said Joe, looking round, and nodding at me with a solemn face.

'Yes, I see,' said I; 'but somebody else – one of the young farmers now, that I saw on the hill, may be stepping in before Christmas.'

'Not they. It's busy times with us these next two months. Besides, I'll look after that. Is it a bargain then?'

'Yes,' said I, 'only mind, Joe, that you look sharp meantime.'

'All right,' said he; and then fell to looking into the fire again: and I sat thinking too, and wondering at my luck, which I could hardly believe in yet.

'And now about the pot,' said Joe; 'suppose Lu says yes, what have you got to keep the pot boiling?'

Then I told him what my salary was, and what I had saved, and where I had put it out, and he nodded away, and seemed very well satisfied.

'Well, Lu has got £500,' said he, 'under father's will. Parson and I are the executors. You must go and see the Parson when you get back to London; he's an out-and-outer, and worth more than all the chaps at that jawing shop of yours put together. The money is out at interest, all but £200, which we've never raised yet, but for that matter I can pay it up whenever it's wanted.'

'Of course,' said I. 'I should wish all her fortune to be settled on her.'

'Yes, I forgot,' said he; 'I suppose there ought to be some sort of tying-up done for the children. So I'll go and see Lawyer Smith about it next market-day.'

'Perhaps you had better wait till after Christmas,' said I.

'Aye, aye,' said he, 'I forgot. We may be running a tail scent after all. But, I say, Dick, if you get married, Lu can never live in those dirty dark streets, and you away all day; she'd mope to death without a place for poultry, and a little bit of turf to cool her feet on.'

'Well,' said I, 'you see I've got a bit of ground under a freehold land society, down the Great Northern line. It's a very pretty place, and only five minutes' walk from a station. I could build a house there in the spring, you know, and have the garden made.'

'That'll do,' said he; 'and if you want £100 or so, to finish it off as should be, why you know where to come for it.'

'Thank you,' said I, 'but I think I can manage it.'

'I shall send her up those Spanish hens,' said he, looking up again presently from his pipe; 'they won't be no use here.'

'I wish, Joe,' said I, 'you wouldn't talk as if it was all quite certain; it makes me feel uncomfortable. Your sister mayn't like me, after all.'

'Makes no odds at all,' said he; 'if she don't have you, there'll be some other chap on in no time. Once a young gal gets a follower it's all over, so fur as I see; though 'tisn't always the first as they takes up with as they sticks to for better for worse.'

'Thank you for nothing, Master Joe,' said I to myself; and I smoked away opposite him for some time without saying a word, thinking what a queer fellow he was, and how I had better let things rest as they were, for I couldn't see how to handle him the least bit in the world; and I can't tell whether I was most glad or sorry, when we heard the fogger come to the kitchen to say the trap was all ready.

Joe knocked the ashes out of his last pipe, took off the last drop out of his tumbler, and then put out his hand and gave me one of his grips.

'It's got to be done,' said he, 'there's no mistake about that.'

'What?' said I, 'what's to be done? Don't look so solemn, Joe, for goodness' sake.'

'It's no laughing matter, mind you,' said he; and he took the candle and went off into the passage, and came back with his whip and two top-coats. 'Here, you get into that,' he went on, handing me one of them; 'you'll find the night rawish.'

I buttoned myself into the coat, which was a white drab one, about as thick as a deal board, with double seams and mother-of-pearl buttons as big as cheese-plates, and followed Joe into the yard with a heavy heart.

'Carpet-bag and hamper in?' said he, taking the reins.

'Ees, Sir, all right.'

'Jump up, Dick.'

I shook hands with the honest fogger, and gave him half-a-crown, which he didn't seem to know how to take; and then I got up by Joe's side, and we walked out of the yard at a foot's pace, on to the grass; he kept off the road to be more quiet. It was bright moonlight, and a streak of white mist lay along the Close. I could hear nothing but the soft crush of the wheels on the rich sward, and the breathing of the great cows as we passed them in the mist. But my heart was beating like a hammer, as I looked back over my shoulder at one window of the old house, until it was hidden behind the elm-trees; and when I jumped down to open the gate into the road, I tore open the great coat, or I think I should have been suffocated.

'It's no laughing matter, mind you,' said Joe, looking round, after we had gone about half-a-mile along the road at a steady trot.

'No, indeed,' said I. I felt much more like crying, and I thought he was trying to comfort me, in his way.

'Come, you button up that coat again, Dick; I won't have you getting into the train at one in the morning with a chill on you. I won't turn my back,' he went on, 'on any man in the county at sampling wheat, or buying a horse, or a lot of heifers, or a flock of sheep. Besides, if a chap does get the blind side of me, it's maybe a ten-pound note lost, and there's an end of it. But when you come to choosing a missus, why, it seems like jumping in the dark, for all as I can see. There's nothing to sample 'em by, and you can't look into their mouths or feel 'em over. I don't take it as a man's judgment's of any account when he comes to that deal – and then, if he does get the wrong sort!'

'Thank you, Joe,' said I, 'but I'm not a bit afraid about getting the wrong sort, if all goes well.'

'No, but I be,' said he; 'why, one would think, Dick, that nobody had to get a missus but you.'

Well, that made me laugh out, I was so tickled to find he was thinking of himself all the time; and for the rest of the drive we were merry enough, for he went on talking about his own prospects so funnily that it was impossible to keep sad or sentimental.

We drew up at the silent station five or six minutes nearly before the train was due, and were received by the one solitary porter.

'What luggage, Sir?' said he to me, as I got down.

'One carpet-bag,' I answered, 'for Paddington.'

'And a hamper,' said Joe; 'you'll find a hamper in behind there. And take care to keep it right side up, porter, for there are some pots of jam in it.'

'Who is it for?' said I; 'can I look after it, and take it anywhere for you?'

'Why, for you, of course,' said Joe; 'you don't suppose the women would have let you go back without some of their kickshaws; and I've had a hare and a couple of chickens put in, and some bacon. You must eat the hare this week, mind.'

I was quite taken by surprise at this fresh instance of the thoughtful kindness of my Vale friends, and wrung Joe's hand, mumbling out something which I meant for thanks.

'Well, good-bye, old fellow,' he said, 'I'm very glad to think you've found your way down at last, and now, don't forget it;' and he gave me a grip which nearly crushed all my knuckles into a jelly, and was gathering up his reins to drive off.

'But Joe, here's your coat,' I called out, and was beginning to take it off – 'you've forgotten your coat.'

'No, no,' said he, 'keep it on – 'twill be very cold tonight, and you'll want it in the train. We'll fetch it at Christmas, and the hamper and the jam pots too, at the same time. Lu will be sure to look after them, so mind you don't lose 'em – Hullo! What in the world are you cutting off the direction for?'

'Oh, it's nothing,' said I, 'but I often fancy parcels go safer with only the railway label on them. Besides, I shall have it in the carriage with me.'

The fact was I had caught sight of the direction, which was in her handwriting, and had quite forgotten Joe, as I was cutting it off to put it in my pocket-book.

'Well, that's a rum start,' said Joe, 'but every one has their own notions about travelling;' and so, with a cheery good-bye to me, off he drove along the dark road: and in another minute the train came up, and I and my luggage were on our way to London.

We went away up through the cold night, eastward, towards the great city which had been my home from childhood. I felt that another man was journeying back from the one who had come down a fortnight before; that he who was travelling eastward had learnt to look beyond his own narrow cellar in the great world-city, to believe in other things than cash payments and shorthand for making his cellar liveable in, to have glimpses of and to sympathise with the life of other men, in his own time, and in the old times before him. These thoughts crowded on me, but all under the shadow of and subordinated to the one great rising hope, in which I had first found and felt my new life. Together they lifted up my heart during the first stages of that night journey, and I opened the window and leant out into the rushing night air, for the carriage was too small for me, and my grand visions and resolves. But soon it began to feel cold, and I shut up the window, and squeezed myself into a corner with my feet up on the opposite seat, and felt very thankful that I had on Joe's great coat. Then the lamp went out, and it got colder as the dawn came on, and my visions and resolves began to get less bright and firm. The other side of the picture rose up in ugly colours, and I thought of the dirty dark clerks' room, and the hours of oil-lamps and bad air, and the heartless whirl and din of the great city. And to crown all came the more than doubt whether my hope would not fade out and die in the recesses of my own heart. What was I? and what my prospects, that any one should ever give me a thought again of those whom I was so fast leaving behind, much more that she, the flower of them all, should single me out before all others? It was absurd, I should most likely never see Elm Close, or the Vale, or the great mysterious Hill again – I had better make up my mind to live the next twenty years as I had the last. With some such meaning spoke the doleful voices, but I was never much of a hand at looking at the doleful side of things, and I made good strong fight on that night ride; and took out my pipe, and lit it, and pressed my back firmer into my corner.

Well, and if they don't remember me, thought I, I can remember them at any rate – they can't help that; and I *will* remember them too, and all their kind pleasant ways, and their manlike games, and their queer songs and stories – and the queen of them all, I can carry her in my heart, thank God for that, and every word I ever heard her speak, and every smile I ever saw light up her merry eyes or dimple round her mouth – and the country, too, the fair rich Vale, and the glorious old Hill, they are mine for ever, and all the memories of the slaying of dragons, and of great battles with the Pagan. I wonder whether I shall ever see the old gentleman again who conjured it up for me, and put life into it, and made me feel as if King Alfred and his Saxons were as near and dear to me as Sir Colin Campbell and the brave lads in India!

Just then the train stopped at Reading, and the guard put his head in to say we stopped for three minutes, and I could get a glass of ale.

So I jumped out and had a glass of ale, and then another; and stamped about the platform till the train started. And when I got into my corner again, I was quite warm and jolly.

I have been always used to a good night's rest, and I daresay the ale made me more sleepy, and so I fell into a kind of doze almost directly. But in my doze the same train of thought went on, and all the people I had been living with and hearing of flitted about in the oddest jumbles, with Elm Close and White Horse Hill for a background. I went through the strangest scenes. One minute I was first cousin to King Alfred, and trying to carry his messages over the Hill to Æthelred, only Joe's old brown horse would run away with me along the Ridgeway; then I was the leader of the Berkshire old gamesters, playing out the last tie with a highwayman, for a gold-laced hat and pair of buckskin breeches; then I was married – I needn't say to whom – and we were keeping house under the Hill, and waiting tea for St George, when he should come down from killing the Dragon. And so it went on, till at last a mist came over the Hill, and all the figures got fainter and fainter, and seemed to be fading away. But as they faded, I could see one great figure coming out clearer through the mist, which I had never noticed before. It was like a grand old man, with white hair and mighty limbs; who looked as old as the hill itself, but yet as if he were as young now as he had ever been, – and at his feet were a pickaxe and spade, and at his side a scythe. But great and solemn as it looked, I felt that the figure was not a man, and I was angry with it, – why should it come in with its great pitiful eyes and smile? why were my brothers and sisters, the men and women, to fade away before it?

'The labour that a man doeth under the sun, it is all vanity. Prince and peasant, the wise man and the fool, they all come to me at last, and I garner them away, and their place knows them no more!' – so the figure seemed to say to itself, and I felt melancholy as I watched it sitting there at rest, playing with the fading figures.

At last it placed one of the little figures on its knee, half in mockery, as it seemed to me, and half in sorrow. But then all changed; and the great figure began to fade, and the small man came out clearer and clearer. And he took no heed of his great neighbour, but rested there where he was placed; and his face was quiet, and full of life, as he gazed steadily and earnestly through the mist. And the other figures came flitting by again, and chanted as they passed, 'The work of one true man is greater than all thy work. Thou hast nought but a seeming power, over it, or over him. Every true man is greater than thee. Every true man shall conquer more than thee; for he shall triumph over death, and hell, and thee, oh, Time!'

And then I woke up, for the train stopped at the place where the tickets are collected; and, in another five minutes, I was in a cab, with my bag and the great basket of country treasures, creeping along in the early November morning towards Gray's Inn Lane. And so ended my fortnight's holiday.

W.J. LINTON

THE SERMON

*LEVITICUS xxiii. v. 1, 2. – And the Lord spake unto Moses, saying, Speak unto the
children of Israel, and say unto them, Concerning the feasts of the Lord which ye shall
proclaim to be holy convocations, even these are my feasts.*

'THESE are *my* feasts,' said God to the nation He was educating; 'keep these feasts,
for they are mine.' Now, what was the nature of these feasts, my brethren, which God
called his? The Bible leaves us in no doubt about them. They were certain seasons set
apart in every year, and at longer intervals, during which the nation was 'to rejoice
before the Lord their God.' Each feast commemorated some event in the nation's life;
either a solemn act of national worship, such as the dedication of the Temple; or some
great national deliverance, such as the Exodus commemorated by the feast of
Passover, or the defeat of Haman's plot in the reign of Ahasuerus, commemorated by
the feast Purim; or the daily care of God for his people, in giving them rain and
fruitful seasons, the harvest and vintage, the increase of corn, and wine, and oil,
commemorated by the feast of Pentecost.

They were *to rejoice* before the Lord their God at all these feasts. With what
outward actions they were to rejoice we are not expressly told; probably it was left to
each generation to express their joy in their own way. In the case of the Passover we
know that they were to eat a lamb and unleavened bread; and we gather, I think, from
many places that both songs and dancing were freely used at the feasts; but further
than this we do not know the outward form of their rejoicing.

But we *do* know the spirit in which they were to keep their feasts, the temper of
mind in which God would have them rejoice before Him. This is most fully
proclaimed. They were to keep alive in themselves and one another the memory of the
great deliverances and blessings, which had been, and were being wrought for them.
They were to remember that these deliverances had been wrought for ignorant
despised bondmen, that these blessings were being poured down on a stiffnecked
sinful people. Remembering these things, they were to come to their feasts, and
rejoice before Him, with humble open hearts, thanking Him for all they possessed,
with love towards their brethren, ready to forgive debts, to help the poor to his right,
and to acknowledge and glory in the bond which bound them all together in one
nation.

Moreover, these feasts were to be feasts for the whole nation – for the rich and the
poor, the free men and the slave, 'for thee, and thy man-servant, and thy
maid-servant;' for those who are in trouble and sorrow, as well as for the prosperous
and happy; 'for the stranger, and fatherless, and widow who are within thy gates.'

One thing more I wish you to notice about the Jewish feasts; they had all the same character, all were God's feasts – not one or two religious feasts, as we should say, and the rest national, but all God's feasts, and all national also. There is no hint in the Bible of any distinction; all feasts ordained for the nation are God's feasts, and their feasts also.

Now such feasts – such rejoicings before the Lord – as these, you can see at once must have had no slight influence on the nation which kept them. Accordingly we find them interwoven with every fibre of the national life: sometimes kept as God's feasts – as He had said they were to be kept – in humbleness and thankfulness, in breaking bonds and forgiving debts; often, as though they had been not His but the devil's feasts, in persecuting prophets and slaying righteous men; and no doubt also, as the natural consequence, in debauchery, gluttony, and hard and usurious dealings with one another; in oppression of man-servant and maid-servant, the widow, the fatherless, and the stranger. But in whatever way the feasts were kept they were always exercising a great power over generation after generation.

I have begun by talking to you about the Jewish feasts, my brethren, because I want to speak to you about our English feasts; and I think if we understand their feasts we shall very likely learn some lessons about our own which may do us good. Now we English, my brethren, as a nation, have neglected this matter of feasts too much. We have very few days on which we rejoice as a nation – in fact the Queen's birthday is almost our only national holiday, and this day we keep as Englishmen, and not as Christians; while the feasts which we keep as Christians, and not as Englishmen (such as Christmas, and Easter, and Whitsuntide), have for this very reason lost much of their worth for us; which we shall recover, when we begin to keep them again, not the less as Christians, but more as Englishmen.

It is my earnest hope and prayer that we may mend in this matter, and that the great Christian festivals and the Queen's birthday may so become all, and more than all, to us and our children, which the Passover and Pentecost were to the Jews. But that it may be so, we must, in this as in all other matters, begin mending at home, in our own families, and our own parishes. And so, my brethren, let us today think about the feasts which we keep who live in this parish, in the Vale of White Horse, who worship in this church.

We all know well enough what these feasts are. First, there is our village feast, a day set apart in every year which is specially *the* feast day of this parish, and of all who belong to it. Then there are our harvest homes, which are not parish but family festivals; when the farmer and those who have worked with him, rejoice together over the garnering in of the fruits which God has given. Lastly, there is the feast which does not come every year, but at longer intervals, the feast of Scouring the White Horse, which is not the feast of one parish, but of the whole country side.

A few words as to the meaning of these feasts of ours. The first is the commemoration of the opening of this parish church, and its dedication to the worship of God. Your harvest homes you know the meaning of as well as I. The third is the commemoration of a great victory, won a thousand years ago by the king of this country against an army of heathen invaders. I remind you of these things because they have been too much forgotten, and we never can rightly use our feasts till we remember them better.

Well, now, remember what I have told you about the Jewish feasts, or rather take your Bible and look for yourselves, whether I tell you the truth, when I say, that our feasts are just such feasts as those which you read of there. The feasts of the Jews were all either feasts in remembrance of the dedication of the Temple, or of thanksgiving for the good gifts of God, or of commemoration for some great national deliverance.

And ours are the very same. Do not think I am dealing unfairly with you in comparing our country feasts to the great national feasts of the Jews. It is not unfair to compare small things with great: families, parishes, nations, must stand or fall by the same laws. A society cannot do evil or good without reaping the fruits thereof, whether it be very small or very great. Do not think that I ought to speak of the great Christian festivals, Christmas and Easter; they are better understood and kept, though very badly as yet. I believe I am taking the right way to make you understand and keep these world-wide Christian feasts properly by bringing you down to these common insignificant feasts of ours, which we, the members of this parish and congregation, have power over; which we can make good or evil; for the use or abuse of which we shall be called to account by God.

For 'thus saith the Lord,' to us as He said to the Jews, 'these are *my* feasts.' They are His, my brethren, whether we like it or not; they are His, though we may try to make them ours, and so make them the devil's. There is no neutral ground, no escape from the hard fact. Let us see now if we cannot accept them, and use them as his. Let us see whether they will be less or more to us if we do so. We shall find the trial worth making I think, in the end.

They are His feasts: how, then, can we come to them as his guests – guests who will be pleasing to Him, who will use his feasts as He would have us? For if we go to a man's feast, the first thing we have to do is to go in such a temper and such a dress as will make us acceptable guests; and shall we do less as the guests of God?

The first thing, then, we have to consider is the temper, the state of mind in which we should go to our feasts; and here; as I said before, the Bible tells us all we want to know. The temper which He required of the Jews, He will require of us. At His feasts we have specially two things to do, to remember and to rejoice. To remember the loving-kindness which He has shown to our fathers and to us, in delivering us many a time from the hand of enemies who were stronger than we; in giving us a Church, where for many hundred years the prayers of generation after generation have gone up to Him, the God of all truth; in giving us the rich increase of His earth, year after year. Remembering these things, then, we are to keep the feast in humility, for our own unworthiness; in thankfulness, for His tender care and unbounded love.

And we are also to rejoice before Him, as members of a family, of a parish, of a country; thinking, therefore, of others, and not of ourselves; making up quarrels, exercising hospitality to all according to our means, seeking to do kindnesses to all who need them, to our debtors, to the oppressed and unfortunate amongst us, to the widows, the fatherless, and the stranger; and in all ways strengthening and deepening the bond which binds us to one another, and to Him.

This, my brethren, is the temper and state of mind which He required of the Jews of old, and which He requires of us at these times especially. Think what our feasts would be, what our whole lives would be, if we tried to remember and to rejoice before the Lord thus.

If we come to His feasts in this temper, my brethren, it matters comparatively little what our outward acts of rejoicing may be. If our hearts are right towards the Lord of the feast and to one another, our dress and actions are surely right also, or will soon become so. Nevertheless, this is a matter of plain, practical importance, and I am not going to shrink from it. I wish to consider with you, how we keep His feasts and our feasts now; whether our method of keeping them is a true expression of that temper and spirit in which they ought to be kept, whether anything better can be suggested.

On these points, as I said above, we have not the same help which we had before. We know very little of how the Jews rejoiced; we may be sure that we are not meant to copy the little we do know, such as the eating of a lamb roasted whole with unleavened bread. It is left for us to find out, and to do, such acts as may be done by those who are humble, and thankful, and loving in heart, towards God and towards each other.

Now there is one thing which one sees at once is wanting in our celebration of these feasts. In the times when they were established, it was the chief act of them, that which gave meaning to them, and kept alive that meaning. We have neglected and disused it, and so they have become all but meaningless to us, mere seasons in which we are to enjoy more pleasures than in ordinary times. This thing which we have forgotten is public fellow-worship, and it ought to be restored as soon as possible. At the yearly meetings of many of your benefit and other clubs, the members go all together to the church, and there worship before attending to their business and their pleasure. Why should not a parish do the same? I know nothing which would so easily and so effectually raise the tone of our village feast as the regular celebration of worship on that day, in the Church, the dedication and consecration of which to the worship of God was the cause of the holiday.

In one respect I believe that we are, to some extent, still keeping the feasts as we ought. I believe that on that day young people who were born in the parish and have left it, make a point, if possible, of getting back to see their fathers and mothers, and friends, and to revive old associations, often bringing with them part of their wages or some present; that many of the silly quarrels and feuds which have arisen during the year are then set to rest; that the residents in the parish make some exertion to welcome their visitors hospitably, and that a general kindly feeling is common throughout the parish. I believe that this is still so, to some extent; but I fear that it is becoming less and less so. My brethren, all this is right, and true, and honest; this is the way to keep God's feasts; you can't go too far in this direction (except by spending more money than you can afford, which is always wrong). But the more you can deepen old family and local ties on these occasions, the more you can heal up quarrels, and forgive debts (both other debts, and money debts – remember that there is no duty more insisted on in God's Word than this of forgiving money debts at these times), and exercise hospitality one to another without grudging, the more will you be keeping God's feasts as He would have you keep them.

Then there are the sports for which prizes are given. There is no need to specify them all, and I shall therefore only speak of the one which is considered the most objectionable – which many people think should be stopped altogether – I mean wrestling. Whatever I may say on this will apply to all the rest. Now, my brethren, are wrestling matches a proper way of keeping God's feasts? That is the question we have to answer.

The object of wrestling and of all other athletic sports is to strengthen men's bodies, and to teach them to use their strength readily, to keep their tempers, to endure fatigue and pain. These are all noble ends, my brethren. God gives us few more valuable gifts than strength of body, and courage, and endurance – to you labouring men they are beyond all price. We ought to cultivate them in all right ways, for they are given us to protect the weak, to subdue the earth, to fight for our homes and country if necessary.

Therefore I say that wrestling, inasmuch as it is a severe trial of strength, temper, and endurance, may be, and ought to be, one of many right and proper ways of rejoicing before God at these feasts. And I say to any man who has strength for it, and can keep his temper, and carries away no vain or proud thoughts if he wins, and no angry or revengeful thoughts if he loses, play by all means. No doubt there are men who ought not to play, who ought to abstain wholly from these games, as some men ought to abstain wholly from drink, who cannot use such things temperately, which is the more worthy and manly way – men so constituted that these sort of games rouse all that is brutal in their natures, others who become braggarts and bullies from success in them. To such men (and each of you can easily find out whether he is such a man) I say abstain wholly.

Having said this, brethren, I must add that great changes should be made in the conduct or management of these games. They should never, on any pretence or plea whatever, be left in the hands of publicans. You should always endeavour to play in sides (as is, I believe, the most common custom) for your county or your parish, and not for yourselves, as you are much more likely in that way to play bravely and fairly. Money prizes should be if possible avoided, for money is the lowest motive for which men can undertake any work or any game. And lastly, every one of you should exercise his whole strength and influence in putting down at once all brutality and bluster and foul play.

As to the rest of the amusements, the visiting shows, the eating and drinking, the dancing and music, I believe them all in themselves to be lawful and right in the sight of God, and fit things to do when we are rejoicing before Him. But, my brethren, I do *not* think them lawful and right, or fit things to be done before anybody but the devil, when they end in such scenes as, I fear – as I know – they often do end in at our feasts. No wonder that the feasts are falling off year by year; that they cease to interest decent and respectable people who used to care about them, when they are deliberately turned by some into scenes of drunkenness and profligacy, which can scarcely be surpassed amongst savages and heathens.

I need not dwell on this, for you all know well enough what I mean. You all know, too – the voice within you tells each of you plainly enough – the moment you are going beyond the proper limits in these matters. It is no use to lay down rules on such subjects. Every man and every woman must be a law to themselves. One can do safely what would ruin another. And here again I say, as I said before, the use of these things is right and good, and what God approves of, who in His infinite love has given us the power of enjoying all these things, and the things themselves to enjoy – music, and dancing, and pleasant company, and food and drink. The abuse of them is of the devil, and destroys body and soul.

I beseech you all to think of what I have said, and endeavour, each in your own way, to retain, or to bring back, if necessary, God's feasts into your own parishes. You, old and grown-up men and women, by living soberly and righteously; never making mischief, or quarrelling; treating your children with forbearance and love, doing your own work, and helping others to do theirs. To you young men, I say, as

Solomon said, rejoice in your youth; rejoice in your strength of body, and elasticity of spirits, and the courage which follows from these; but remember that for these gifts you will be judged – not condemned, mind, but judged. You will have to show before a Judge who knoweth your inmost hearts, that you have used these His great gifts well; that you have been pure, and manly, and true.

And to you, young women, I can but say the same. Beauty, and purity, and youth, and merry light hearts, and all the numberless attractions which have been poured upon you, are tremendous influences for good or evil, – gifts for which you will have to give an account. Rejoice in them; use them freely; but avoid, as you would death itself, all rivalry with one another, all attempts to exercise power over men you do not care for, every light thought, and word, and look. For the light word or look is but a step from the impure, and the experience of the whole world is telling you

> How mirth can into folly glide,
> And folly into sin.

But now to conclude. You may ask, how are we all to keep these things in mind? how, when we are all met together to enjoy ourselves, can we be ever on the watch for this evil, which you say is so near us? You cannot, my brethren; but One is with you, is in you, who can and will, if you will let Him.

Men found this out in the old time, and have felt it and known it ever since. Three thousand years ago this truth dawned upon the old Psalmist, and struck him with awe. He struggled with it; he tried to escape from it, but in vain. 'Whither shall I go then,' he says, 'from Thy spirit? or whither shall I flee them from Thy presence? If I go up to heaven, Thou art there: if I go down to hell, Thou are there also. If I take the wings of the morning, and reside in the uttermost parts of the sea; even there also shall Thy hand lead me, and Thy right hand shall hold me.'

Is any of us stronger or wiser than the Psalmist? Is there any place for us to flee to, which was not open to him? My brethren, had we not better make up our minds to accept and acknowledge the truth, to which our own consciences bear witness; that, not only in heaven, and in hell, and in the uttermost parts of sea and earth, He is present, but that in the inmost recesses of our own hearts there is no escape from His Spirit – that He is there also, sustaining us, pleading with us, punishing us.

We know it by the regret we feel for time wasted and opportunities neglected; by the loathing coming back to us, time after time, for our every untrue or mean thought, word, or deed; by every longing after truth, and righteousness, and purity, which stirs our sluggish souls. By all these things, and in a thousand other ways, we feel it, we know it.

Let us, then, come to our feasts owning this, and giving ourselves up to His guidance. At first it will be hard work; our will and spirits will be like a lump of ice in a man's hand, which yields but slowly to the warm pressure. But do not despair; throw yourselves on His guidance, and He will guide you, He will hide you under His wings, you shall be safe under His feathers, His faithfulness and truth shall be your shield and buckler.

The ice will melt into water, and the water will lie there in the hollow of the hand, moving at the slightest motion, obeying every impulse which is given to it.

My brethren, the Spirit of God which is in every one of us – the Spirit of truth and love unchangeable – will take possession of our spirits, if we will but let Him, and turn not only our feasts into feasts of the Lord, but our whole lives into the lives of children of God, and joint-heirs of heaven with his Son.

APPENDIX

THE earliest authentic historical notices of the White Horse are, so far as I am aware, –

1st. A Cartulary of the Abbey of Abingdon, now in the British Museum, of the time of Henry II, the exact date of it being, it is believed, AD 1171. It runs as follows – 'Consuetudinis apud Anglos tunc erat, ut monachi qui vellent pecuniarum patrimoniorum qui forent susceptibiles, ipsisque fruentes quomodo placeret dispensarent. Unde et in Abbendonia duo, Leofricus et Godricus Cild appellati, quorum unus Godricus, Spersholt juxta locum qui vulgo mons Albi Equi nuncupatur, alter Leofricus Hwitceorce super flumen Tamisie maneria sita patrimoniali jure obtinebant,' &c.

2dly. Another Cartulary of the same Abbey, of the reign of Richard I, which runs as follows: – 'Prope montem ubi ad Album Equum scanditur, ab antiquo tempore Ecclesia ista manerium Offentum appellatum in dominio possidet, juxta quod villa X hidarum adjacet ex jure Ecclesiæ quam Speresholt nominavit,' &c.

3dly. An entry on the Close Rolls, 42 Ed. III. or AD 1368–9 – 'Gerard de l'Isle tient en la vale de White Horse one fee,' &c. See Archæologia, vol. xxxi. p. 290. Letter from William Thoms, Esq. to J.Y. Ackerman, Esq. Secretary.

Coming down to comparatively modern times, it is curious that so little notice should have been taken of the White Horse by our antiquaries. Wise in his Letter to Dr. Mead (1738), which has been already quoted from in the text, regrets this, and then adds, 'Leland's journey does not seem to have carried him this way, nor does Camden here go out of the other's track; though he mentions upon another occasion, and by the bye, *The White Horse*; but in such a manner, that I could wish, for his own sake, he had passed it over in silence with the rest. For his own account is altogether so unbecoming so faithful and accurate an author, insinuating to his readers that it has no existence but in the imagination of country people. *"The Thames,"* says he, *"falls into a valley, which they call* The Vale of White Horse *from I know not what shape of a Horse fancied on the side of a whitish Hill."* Much nearer to the truth is Mr Aubrey, however wide of the mark, who in the additions to the Britannia says: "I leave others to determine, whether the White Horse on the Hill was made by Hengist, since the Horse was the arms or figure in Hengist's standard." The author of a "Tour through England" is a little more particular, though he leaves us as much in the dark about the antiquity and design of it. "Between this town of Marlborow and Abingdon, is the Vale of White Horse. The inhabitants tell a great many fabulous stories of the original of its name; but there is nothing of foundation in them, that I could find. The whole of the story is this: Looking south from the Vale, we see a trench cut on the side of a high green hill, in the shape of a horse, and not ill-shaped neither; the trench is about a yard deep, and filled almost up with chalk, so that at a distance you see the exact shape of a White Horse, but so large, as to take up near an acre of ground, some say almost two acres. From this figure the Hill is called in our maps White Horse Hill, and the low or flat country under it the Vale of White Horse."' (See pp. 21, 22.)

NOTE II

Medeshamstede, however, was restored with great splendour in the year 963. The account in the Saxon Chronicle is so illustrative of what was going on in England at the time that I think I may be allowed to give it, especially as the restoration was the work of a Vale of White Horse man, Ethelwold, Abbot of Abingdon, who was in this year made Bishop of Winchester.

Edgar was king, and Dunstan Archbishop of Canterbury – Ethelwold after strong measures at Winchester (where 'he drove the clerks out of the bishopric because they would not observe any rule, and he set the monks there'), 'went to the king and begged of him that he would give him all the minsters which heathen men had of old time broken down, because he would restore them; and the king joyfully granted it.' Then he restored Ely, and 'after that came Bishop Ethelwold to the minster which was called Medeshamstede, which of old time had been destroyed by heathen men. He found nothing there but old walls and wild woods. There found he hidden in the old walls writings that Abbot Hudda had erewhile written, how king Wulfhere and Ethelred his brother had built it, and how they had freed it against king and against bishop, and against all secular service, and how the pope Agatho had confirmed the same by his rescript, and the archbishop "deo dedit." Then caused he the minster to be built, and set there an abbot who was called Adulf, and caused monks to be there where before was nothing. Then came he to the king and caused him to look at the writings which before were found, and the king answered then and said, I, Edgar, grant and give today before God and before the Archbishop Dunstan, freedom to St Peter's minster, from king and from bishop, and all the villages that lie thereto, that is to say, Eastfield, and Dodthorp, and Eye, and Paxton. And thus I free it, that no bishop have there any command without the abbot of the minster. And I give the town which is called Oundle, with all which thereto lieth, that is to say, that which is called "the eight hundreds," and market and toll so freely that neither king, nor bishop, nor earl, nor sheriff have there any command, nor any man except the Abbot alone and him whom he thereto appointeth' – and after giving other lands to Christ and St Peter through the prayer of Bishop Ethelwold, 'with sack and sock, toll and team, and infangthief,' and willing 'that a market be in the same town, and no other be between Stamford and Huntingdon,' the king ends: – 'And I will that all liberties and all the remissions that my predecessors have given, that they stand, and I sign and confirm it with Christ's rood token. ✠' 'Then Dunstan the Archbishop of Canterbury answered and said, I grant that all the things which are here given and spoken of and all the things which thy predecessors and mine have conceded, those will I that they stand: and whosoever this breaketh, then give I him the curse of God, and of all saints, and of all ordained heads, and of myself, unless he come to repentance. And I give in acknowledgement to St Peter my mass-hackel, and my stole, and my reef, for the service of Christ.' 'I, Oswald, Archbishop of York, assent to all these words, by the holy rood which Christ suffered on. ✠ 'I, Ethelwold, bless all who shall observe this, and I excommunicate all who shall break this, unless he come to repentance.' So the minster at Medeshamstede was set up again under Adulf, who bought lands and greatly enriched it, till Oswald died, and he was chosen Archbishop of York, and was succeeded as abbot by Kenulph, who 'first made the will about the minster; then gave he that to name Peterborough which was before called Medeshamsted.' – *Saxon Chronicle* AD 963.

NOTE III

SITE OF THE BATTLE OF ASHDOWN

There are four spots in Berkshire which claim the honour of being the Œscendun of the chroniclers, where Æthelred and Alfred gained their great victory; they are Ilsley, Ashamstead, Aston in the parish of Bluberry, and Ashdown, close to White Horse Hill. Now it seems clear that Ashdown was, in Saxon times, the name of a district stretching over a considerable portion of the Berkshire chalk range, and it is quite possible that all of the above sites may have been included in that district; therefore, I do not insist much upon the name, though whatever weight is to be attached to it, must tell in favour of the latter site, that of Ashdown. Let us, however, consider the other qualifications of the rival sites.

That of Ilsley is supported, so far as I know, only by Hewitt in his antiquities of the Hundred of Compton (1844); and his argument rests chiefly on the fitness of the ground for the scene of a great battle. He tells us that the detachments of three Waterloo regiments, marching through Ilsley in 1816, when they came to the spot, stopped and called out, 'Waterloo! Waterloo!' to one another. He also states that the name Ilsley is, in fact, 'Hilde læg,' the field of battle; but as he has no tradition in his favour, and cannot, so far as I know, point to any remains in the neighbourhood in support of his theory, I think his case must fail, and only mention it to show that I have not overlooked the claim.

Ashamstead, situate five miles to the south-east of Ilsley, is named by the Lysons in their topographical account of Berkshire as the probable site of the battle, but they give no reasons, and are unsupported by tradition or remains.

Aston has a stronger case. It is situate between Wallingford and Ilsley. The range of chalk hills rises just above it, and one detached hill is here thrown out into the vale, on which are still visible considerable earthworks. There is a chapel called Thorn Chapel on the easter slope of this hill, and I am told there is a tradition that this chapel was built on the spot where some Saxon king heard mass on the morning of a battle. It is suggested by Mr Lousley and others, that the Saxons occupied this outlying hill, the Danes the opposite range; and that the battle was fought in the valley between, where, when the road was recently altered, a number of bones were found, apparently thrown in together without care, as would be the case after a battle. There are, however, no regular barrows or other remains. Bishop Gibson is in favour of this spot, on account, as it would seem, of a passage in the Saxon chronicle for the year 1006, which runs as follows: 'They' (the Danes) 'turned *along Ashdown* to Cwichelmes Low.'

The bishop says, that Cwichelmes Low (the *low* or hill of King Cwichelm, who

reigned in these parts, and died in the year 636 AD) is Cuckhamsley Hill, or
Scuchamore Knob, as it is generally called; a high hill in the same chalk range, about
ten miles east of White Horse Hill; and he argues that, as the Danes went *from*
Wallingford, *by* Ashdown, *to* Cwichelmes Low, we must look for Ashdown between
Wallingford and Cuckhamsley Hill. Now Aston lies directly between the two,
therefore Aston is Ashdown, and the site of the battle. But the place now called
Ashdown is on the further side of Cuckhamsley Hill from Wallingford – therefore the
Danes could not have passed it in getting from Wallingford to Cuckhamsley Hill –
therefore the modern Ashdown cannot be the site of the battle.

To this I answer, *First*, the Bishop *assumes* that Cwichelmes Low is Cuckhamsley
Hill, without giving any reason.

Secondly, assuming Cwichelmes Low and Cuckhamsley Hill to be identical; yet, as
Ashdown was clearly a large tract of country, the Danes might go from Wallingford,
along a part of it, *to* Cwichelmes Low without passing the battle-field.

Thirdly, the name Aston is written 'Estone' in Domesday Book; meaning 'East
Town,' or enclosure, and not 'Mons fraxini,' the 'Hill of the Ash-tree.'

Fourthly, Æthelred and Alfred would have kept to the hills in their retreat, and
never have allowed the Danes to push them out into the Thames-valley, where the
Pagan cavalry would have been invaluable; but this must have been the case, if we
suppose Aston to be the site of the battle. Lastly, all the above sites are too near to
Reading, the farthest being only sixteen miles from that town. But Æthelred and
Alfred had been retreating three days, and would therefore much more probably be
found at Ashdown by White Horse Hill, which is ten miles farther along the range of
hills.

Ashdown, the remaining site, and the one which I believe to be the true one, is the
down which surrounds White Horse Hill, in the parish of Uffington. On the highest
point of the hill, which is 893 feet above the level of the sea, stands Uffington Castle, a
plain of more than eight acres in extent, surrounded by earthworks, and a single deep
ditch, which Camden, and other high authorities, say are Danish.

There is another camp, with earthworks, called Hardwell-camp, about a mile WNW
of Uffington Castle, and a third smaller circular camp, called King Alfred's camp, about
a mile to the SW, which may still be made out, close to the wall of Ashdown Park, Lord
Craven's seat, although Aubrey says, that in his time the works were 'almost quite
defaced, by digging for the Sarsden stones to build my Lord Craven's house in the Park.'
Wise suggests that the Danes held Uffington Castle; that Æthelred was in Hardwell-
camp, and Alfred in Alfred's camp. A mile and a half to the eastward, in which direction
the battle must have rolled, as the Saxons slowly gained the day, is a place called the
Seven Barrows, where are seven circular burial-mounds, and several other large
irregularly-shaped mounds, full of bones; the light soil which covers the chalk is actually
black around them. The site agrees in all points with the description in the chroniclers; it
is the upper distance from Reading; the name is the one used by the chroniclers, –
'Ash-down,' 'Mons Fraxini,' 'Æscendun;' it is likely that Æthelred would have fought
somewhere hereabouts to protect Wantage, a royal burg, and his birthplace, which
would have been otherwise at the mercy of the enemy; and lastly, there – and not at
Cuckhamsley Hill, or elsewhere – is carved the White Horse, which has been from time
immemorial held to be a monument of the great victory of Ashdown. For the above
reasons, I think we are justified in claiming this as the site of the battle.

NOTE IV

WAYLAND SMITH'S CAVE

Wise (see p. 00) says he thinks he has discovered the place of burial of King Basreg, Bagseeg (or whatever his name might be, for it is given in seven or eight different ways in the chroniclers), in Wayland Smith's cave, which place he describes as follows: –

'The place is distinguished by a parcel of stones set on edge, and enclosing a piece of ground raised a few feet above the common level, which every one knows was the custom of the Danes, as well as of some other northern nations. And Wormius observes, that if any Danish chief was slain in a foreign country, they took care to bury him as pompously as if he had died in his own. Mr Aubrey's account of it is this: "About a mile [or less] from the Hill [White Horse Hill] there are a great many large stones, which, though very confused, must yet be laid there on purpose. Some of them are placed edgewise, but the rest are so disorderly that one would imagine they were tumbled out of a cart." The disorder which Mr Aubrey speaks of is occasioned by the people having thrown down some of the stones (for they all seem originally to have been set on edge), and broken them to pieces to mend their highways. Those that are left enclose a piece of ground of an irregular figure at present, but which formerly might have been an oblong square, extending only north and south.

'On the east side of the southern extremity stand three squarish flat stones of about four or five feet over each way, set on edge, and supporting a fourth of much larger dimensions, lying flat upon them. These altogether form a cavern or sheltering-place, resembling pretty exactly those described by Wormius, Bartholine, and others, except in the dimensions of the stones; for whereas this may shelter only ten or a dozen sheep from a storm, Wormius mentions one in Denmark that would shelter a hundred.

'I know of no other monument of this sort in England: but in Wales and the Isle of Anglesey there are several not unlike it, called by the natives *Cromlechs*. The Isle of Anglesey having been the chief seat of the Druids, induced its learned antiquary to ascribe them to the ancient Britons; an assertion that I will not take upon me to contradict, but shall only at this time observe, that I find sufficient authorities to convince me that ours must be Danish.

'Whether this remarkable piece of antiquity ever bore the name of the person here buried is not now to be learned, the true meaning of it being long since lost in ignorance and fable. All the account which the country people are able to give of it is, "At this place lived formerly an invisible smith; and if a traveller's horse had lost a shoe upon the road, he had no more to do than to bring the horse to this place, with a piece of money, and leaving both there for some little time, he might come again and find the money gone, but the horse new shod." The stones standing upon the *Rudge-way*, as it is called (which was the situation that they chose for burial monuments), I suppose gave occasion to the whole being called Wayland Smith, which is the name it was always known by to the country people.

'An English antiquary might find business enough who should attempt to unriddle all the fabulous traditions of the vulgar, which ascribe these works of unknown antiquity to demons and invisible powers.

'Leaving, therefore, the story of the invisible smith to be discussed by those who have more leisure, I only remark, that these stones are, according to the best Danish antiquaries, a burial altar; that their being raised in the midst of a plain field, near the great road, seems to indicate some person there slain, and buried, and that this person was probably a chief or king; there being no monument of this sort near that place, perhaps not in England, beside.' (See pp. 25, 26, 27.)

I have given Wise's statement of his own case, but the better opinion amongst antiquaries seems to be that he is wrong, and that the cromlech called Wayland Smith's Cave is of much earlier date than 871 AD.

I insert here the note from Kenilworth (note B, p. 218) in which Sir Walter Scott mentions Wayland Smith's Cave: –

'The great defeat given by Alfred to the Danish invaders, is said by Mr Gough to have taken place near Ashdown in Berkshire. The burial place of Bœreg, the Danish chief who was slain in this fight, is distinguished by a parcel of stones, less than a mile from the hill, set on edge, enclosing a piece of ground somewhat raised. On the east side of the southern extremity, stand three squarish flat stones, of about four or five feet over either way, supporting a fourth, and now called by the vulgar Wayland Smith, from an idle tradition about an invisible smith replacing lost horse-shoes there.' (Gough's edition of Camden's *Britannica*. Vol. I. p. 221.)

'The popular belief still retains memory of this wild legend, which, connected as it is with the site of a Danish sepulchre, may have arisen from some legend concerning the northern Duergar, who resided in the rocks, and were cunning workers in steel and iron. It was believed that Wayland Smith's fee was sixpence, and that, unlike other workmen, he was offended if more was offered. Of late his offices have been again called to memory; but fiction has in this, as in other cases, taken the liberty to pillage the stores of oral tradition. This monument must be very ancient, for it has been kindly pointed out to me that it is referred to in an ancient Saxon charter as a landmark. The monument has been of late cleared out, and made considerably more conspicuous.'

It will be seen from this that Sir Walter assumes the view of Wise to be correct, but he never saw the place.

NOTE V

As an illustration of one of the methods by which traditions are kept up in the country, I insert some verses written by Job Cork, an Uffington man of two generations back, who was a shepherd on White Horse Hill for fifty years.

It was early one summer's morn,
The weather fine and very warm,

A stranger to White Horse Hill did go
To view the plains and fields below.

As he along the hill did ride,
Taking a view on every side,
The which he did so much enjoy
Till a shepherd's dog did him annoy.

At length an aged man appeared,
A watching of his fleecy herd,
With threadbare coat and downcast eye,
To which the stranger did draw nigh.

'O noble shepherd, can you tell
How long you kept sheep on this hill?'
'Zeven Year in Zundays I have been
A shepherd on this hill so green.'

'That is a long time, I must own,
You have kept sheep upon this down;
I think that you must have been told
Of things that have been done of old.'

'Ah, Zur, I can remember well
The stories the old voke do tell –
Upon this hill which here is seen
Many a battle there have been.

'If it is true so I heard zay,
King Gaarge did here the dragon slay,
And down below on yonder hill
They buried him as I heard tell.

'If you along the Rudgeway go,
About a mile for aught I know,
There Wayland's Cave then you may see
Surrounded by a group of trees.

'They say that in this cave did dwell
A smith that was invisible;
At last he was found out, they say,
He blew up the place and vlod away.

'To Devonshire then he did go,
Full of sorrow, grief, and woe,
Never to return again,
So here I'll add the shepherd's name –

JOB CORK.'

There is no merit in the lines beyond quaintness; but they are written in the sort of jingle which the poor remember; they have lived for fifty years and more, and will probably, in quiet corners of the Vale, outlive the productions of much more celebrated verse-makers than Job Cork though probably they were never reduced into writing until written out at my request.

Job Cork was a village humorist, and stories are still told of his sayings, some of which have a good deal of fun in them: I give one example in the exact words in which it was told to me: –

'One night as Job Cork came off the downs, drough-wet to his very skin, it happened his wife had been a baking. So, when he went to bed, his wife took his leather breeches, and put 'em in the oven to dry 'em. When he woke in the morning he began to feel about for his thengs, and he called out, and zed, "Betty, where be mee thengs?" "In the oven," zed his wife. Zo he looked in the oven and found his leather breeches all cockled up together like a piece of parchment, and he bawled out, "O Lard! O Lard! what be I to do? Was ever man plagued as I be?" "Patience, Job, patience, Job," zed his wife; "remember thy old namesake, how he was plagued." "Ah!" zed the old man, "a was plagued surely; but his wife never baked his breeches."'

Other shepherds of the Hill have been poets in a rough sort of way. I add one of their home-made songs, as I am anxious to uphold the credit of my countrymen as a tuneful race.

Come, all you shepherds as minds for to be,
  You must have a gallant heart,
You must not be down-hearted,
  You must a-bear the smart;
You must a-bear the smart, my boys,
  Let it hail or rain or snow,
For there is no ale to be had on the Hill
  Where the wintry wind doth blow.

When I kept sheep on White Horse Hill
  My heart began to ache,
My old ewes all hung down their heads,
  And my lambs began to bleat.
Then I cheered up with courage bold,
  And over the Hill did go,
For there is no ale to be had on the Hill
  When the wintry wind doth blow.

I drive my sheep into the fold,
  To keep them safe all night,
For drinking of good ale, my boys,
  It is my heart's delight.
I drove my sheep into the fold,

And homeward I did go,
For there is no ale to be had on the Hill
  When the wintry wind doth blow.

We shepherds are the liveliest lads
  As ever trod English ground,
If we drops into an ale-house
  We values not a crownd.
We values not a crownd, my boys,
  We'll pay before we go,
For there is no ale to be had on the Hill
  When the wintry wind doth blow.'

THE END

POACHER'S PIE

FRED ARCHER

Poachers, princes and plum-pickers all have their say in this book by Fred Archer which celebrates the lives of the little master men who grew their asparagus and cabbages on the black soil of the Vale of Evesham. He writes of the market gardeners, upright and industrious, and of the men who worked for them, like Kick Pudding, the student of Darwin. And he tells of the farmers who considered themselves above cabbages, employed the farm labourers in their tied cottages, and hunted with the emigré French dukes. These Orleanist princes lived in great style just down the Worcester road at Wood Norton Hall, entertained the crowned heads of Europe to hunting and shooting and provided the folk of Evesham and Ashton with jobs, certainly, but also with an endless source of enjoyable and scandalous speculation in the Whistling Ploughman or the Jolly Gardeners.

The well-stocked coverts of Wood Norton also provided temptation and the killing of one of the Duke's keepers resulted in a murder trial at Worcester assizes in 1890. In the powerful centrepiece of his book, Fred Archer retells the whole stark story of the poacher brothers, Sam and Joe Boswell and their accomplice Lovely Hill, from the newspaper reports of the time and from the memories of people, including his own mother and uncle, who knew the families involved.

Poacher's Pie is a book of riches, teeming with people from every walk of life in Fred Archer's Cotswolds.

176pp   216mm × 135mm
ISBN 0 86299 428 4 (paper) £4.95

THE LOST VILLAGES OF ENGLAND

MAURICE BERESFORD

Among existing villages in the English countryside are the sites of many others which have not
been fortunate enough to survive, though six
hundred years or so ago they were little different
from their neighbours. In this classic pioneering
study, Professor Beresford has located these lost
villages and he describes the occasion of their
depopulation and the character of those who
destroyed them.

Aerial photographs and ground plans of char-
acteristic sites are given, together with maps to
show the local distribution of lost villages. A
gazetteer is included giving listings by county,
with map references for identification.

445pp   216mm × 138mm
Illustrated
ISBN 0 86299 108 0 (paper) £8.95

EXPLORING VILLAGES

JOSCELYNE FINBERG

Exploring Villages explains the significance and the history of the various elements to be found in villages. In successive chapters it discusses the natural landscape and the imprint which man has made on it. From farms, fields, hedges, roads, houses, schools, churches, and even the unmellowed productions of her own age, small facts are drawn and the history of a village pieced together.

In recent years people have become increasingly aware that history is all around them, and interest in the subject continues to grow. Many villages are now engaged in reconstructing their own history, and teachers find their students take a keen interest in this type of project. This book will be invaluable to anyone engaged in such an enterprise.

264pp   216mm × 135mm
Illustrated
ISBN 0 86299 346 6 (paper) £6.95

UNCLE GEORGE AND COMPANY

HUMPHREY PHELPS

Uncle George is back. That lovable old rogue who surfaced in Humphrey Phelp's previous stories of country and farming life. *Just Across The Fields, Just Over Yonder* and *Just Where We Belong*, now has a book all to himself.

Some time before the war Uncle George threatened to finish with baking – although, some say, the way he was running it in those last few years, it had almost finished with him too. He became a full-time smallholder, able to follow his natural bent and indulge in all his favourite pastimes.

A shed stood in the garden covered in honeysuckle and it was here that Uncle George pondered upon the strange ways of the world and men, and the stranger, unfathomable ways of women. (He was a bachelor and rather wary of women in general.) It was here also that he spent his time thinking of new schemes or even newer schemes when the earlier ones went awry as they sometimes did. And there are lots of schemes and adventures in this rollicking and affectionate portrait.

160pp   216mm × 135mm
ISBN 0 86299 444 6 (paper) £4.95

THE FLOWER OF GLOSTER

E. TEMPLE THURSTON

In 1911 Temple Thurston hired a canal boat, *The Flower of Gloster* and travelled the waterways of central England.

From Oxford he and his barge companion, Eynsham Harry, drifted northwards to Warwick and Stratford-on-Avon, then south-westwards to Tewkesbury and finally through the Golden Valley and Sapperton Tunnel to Lechlade.

It was probably the last time such a journey could be made, through a countryside and waterways system that had remained unchanged from the dawn of the canal age. As such, his record of their travels remains unique in its description of the rural scene and the way of life of the boat people.

176pp   248mm × 172mm
Illustrated
ISBN 0 86299 305 9 (paper) £6.95

YAP

JAN STEWER

This book contains a collection of humorous tales of Devon village life, told in the tongue of the native. The dialect, however, is never obscure and the meaning is always perfectly simple to follow.

Included among these yarns are the amusing account of Jan Stewer playing golf; of the great singing contest between the villages of Pitt Wollidge and Stoke Arrish; of the strange issue of the fortune telling of Abdul the Prophet and of Silas Wonnacott's only performance as a 'waxworks'.

Jan Stewer's tales of Devon village life are relished by every true Devonian, although they are by no means restricted to folk from that county, but are greatly appreciated by everyone with a taste for simple tales of simple life.

160pp 216mm × 135mm
ISBN 0 86299 431 4 (paper) £4.95

FIELDS IN THE
ENGLISH LANDSCAPE

CHRISTOPHER TAYLOR

Fields are one of the most familiar features of
the English landscape and give the countryside
much of its diversity of scenery. They provide a
fascinating variety of shapes and sizes which
reflect developments over thousands of years.

In *Fields in the English Landscape* a leading
archaeologist and local historian shows how
English fields have evolved from prehistoric
times to the present day, with special emphasis
on what remains to be seen today. He interprets
the different kinds of evidence available,
whether the physical remains of Prehistoric and
Roman England and the Dark Ages, or the
increasing amount of written documentation
for the medieval and later periods, and
examines the relevance of the role played by
boundaries.

Fields are a record for the historian and the
author throws important light on such topics as
the so-called Celtic fields, early medieval open
fields and Parliamentary enclosure. He
examines features of the land which have been
altered by generations of agricultural practice
and resulted in today's paddocks, water-
meadows, terraces and the common ridge-and-
furrow.

192pp   216mm × 135mm
ISBN 0 86299 449 7 (paper) £6.95